CONTENTS

MW01000282

ISBN 0-8497-6276-6

Unit 1
Hemiola

Hemiola is a change of meter that occurs without a change of time signature. The change is usually from triple meter to duple meter or vice versa. The change of meter is created by the displacement of strong and weak beats through use of accent signs or by the grouping of notes in the melodic line.

In the example below, the hemiola is created with the use of accent signs (*fz*). The numbers above the staff show the counts according to the time signature, and the counts below the staff show the change to simple duple meter.

From *Impromptu, Op. 90, No. 4,* by Schubert
(*Piano Repertoire: Romantic & 20th Century,* Level 10, page 7)

In the second measure of the example below, the hemiola is created by the grouping of notes in the melodic line. The numbers above the staff show the counts according to the time signature, and the counts below the staff show the change from compound duple to simple triple meter.

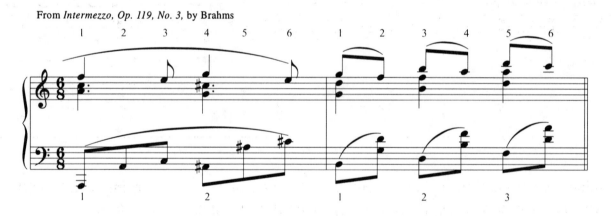

From *Intermezzo, Op. 119, No. 3,* by Brahms

In the example below, the hemiola is created by the grouping of notes in the second measure. The numbers inside the staff show the counts according to the time signature, and the counts below the staff show the change from simple triple to compound duple meter.

From *Courante (English Suite No. 2)* by Bach

1. In the music excerpt below, the hemiola is created with accents in measures 1-2, and then by the grouping of notes in the melodic line in measures 3-4. Notice that the hemiola is only in the right hand while the left hand remains in triple meter. Write the counts according to the time signature on the line below the staff. Write the hemiola counts on the lines inside the staff.

From *Waltz* by Poulenc
(*Piano Repertoire: Romantic & 20th Century,* Level 9, page 69)

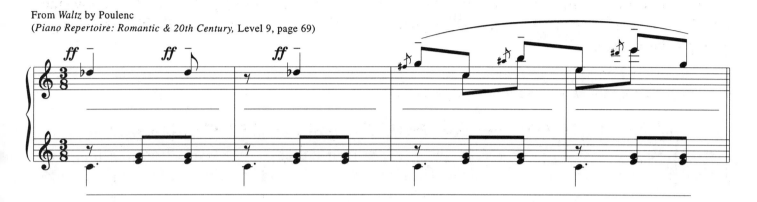

2. In the music excerpt below, the hemiola is created by the grouping of notes in the melodic line of the left hand. Write the counts according to the time signature on the lines inside the staff. Write the hemiola counts on the line under the staff.

From *Sonata, Op. 79,* by Beethoven
(*Piano Repertoire: Baroque & Classical,* Level 9, page 63)

3. Determine the correct time signature for the music example below by writing counts on the lines above and below the staff. Write the time signature at the beginning of the staff.

From *Intermezzo, Op. 119, No. 3,* by Brahms

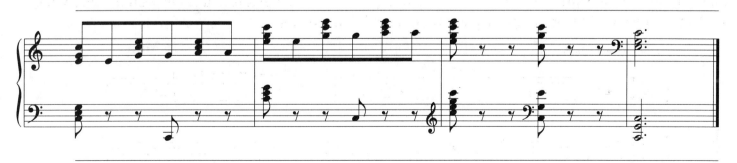

Unit 2
Key Signatures

The Circle of Keys

The **circle of keys** is a diagram of all Major and minor key signatures. The sharp keys are arranged from the top, moving clockwise. The flat keys are arranged from the top, moving counter clockwise.

There are fifteen Major keys: seven sharp keys, seven flat keys, and one key with no sharps or flats. Likewise, there are fifteen relative minor keys.

The keys at the bottom of the circle are called **enharmonic** keys because their tones sound the same but are named and written differently.

The circle of keys is sometimes called the **circle of fifths** because the keys are arranged an interval of a fifth apart. Notice that as you move around the circle clockwise from the top, one new sharp is added to each key. As you move around the circle counter clockwise from the top, one new flat is added to each key.

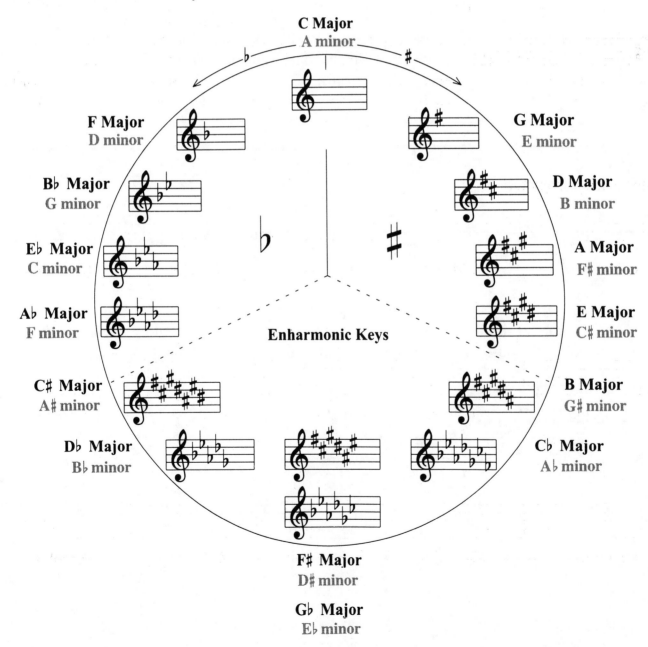

1. Write the Major and minor name for each key signature.

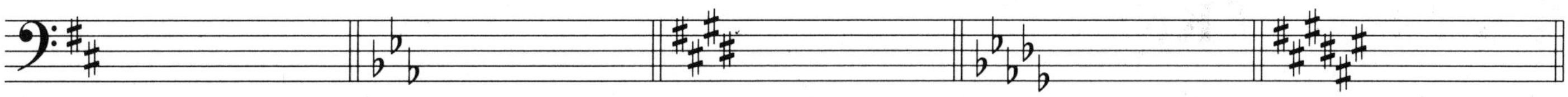

____ Major	____ Major	____ Major	____ Major	____ Major
____ minor	____ minor	____ minor	____ minor	____ minor

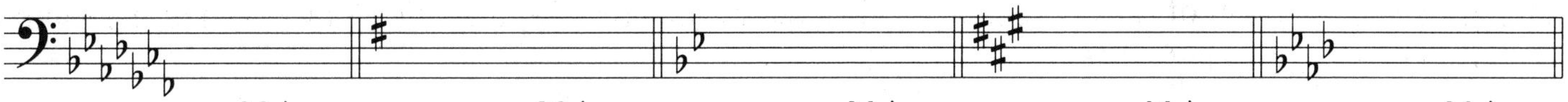

____ Major	____ Major	____ Major	____ Major	____ Major
____ minor	____ minor	____ minor	____ minor	____ minor

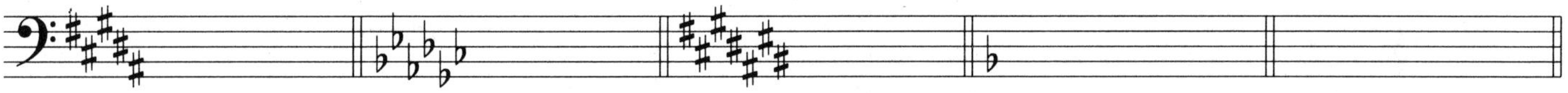

____ Major	____ Major	____ Major	____ Major	____ Major
____ minor	____ minor	____ minor	____ minor	____ minor

2. Write each key signature.

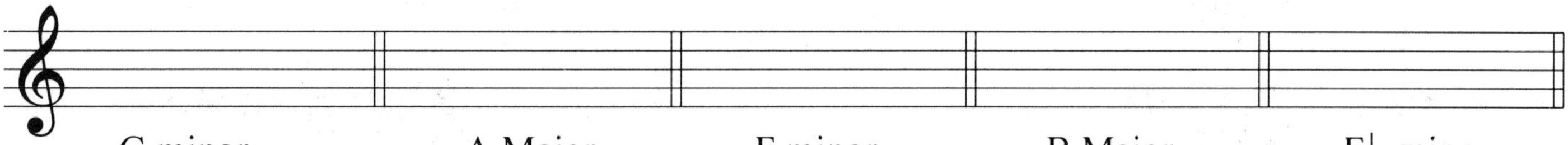

G minor	A Major	F minor	B Major	E♭ minor

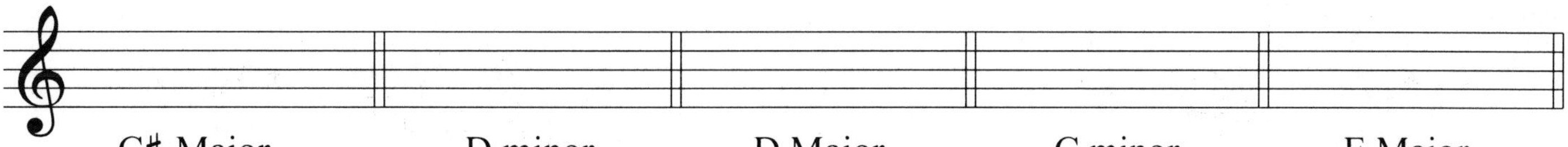

C♯ Major	D minor	D Major	C minor	E Major

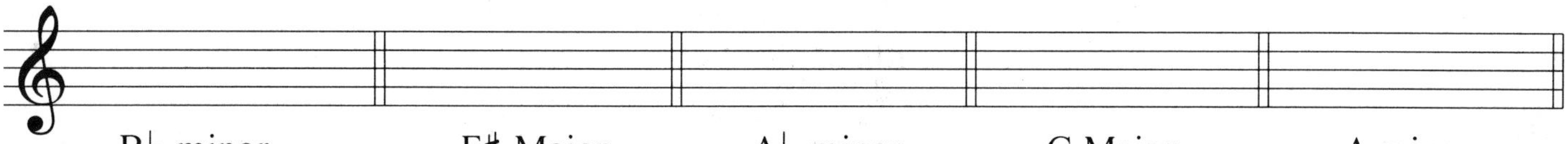

B♭ minor	F♯ Major	A♭ minor	G Major	A minor

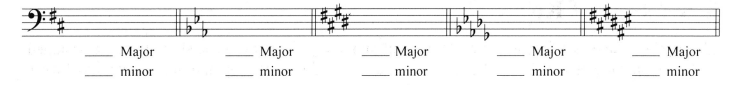

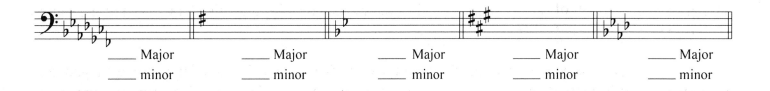

Unit 3
Scales

Major Scales

All **Major scales** are formed with the same pattern of half steps and whole steps:

whole - whole - **half** - whole - whole - whole - **half**

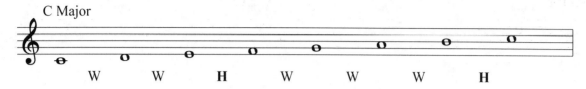

1. Add the correct sharps or flats to form each Major scale (do not use a key signature). Check your answers by referring to the Circle of Keys on page 4.

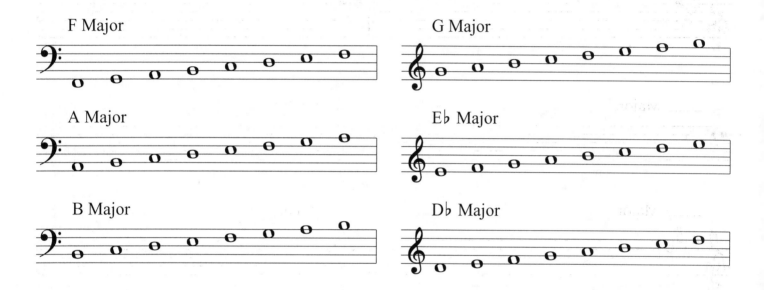

2. Draw the notes of each Major scale ascending. Use whole notes. Add the correct sharps or flats to form each scale (do not use a key signature). Check your answers by referring to the Circle of Keys on page 4.

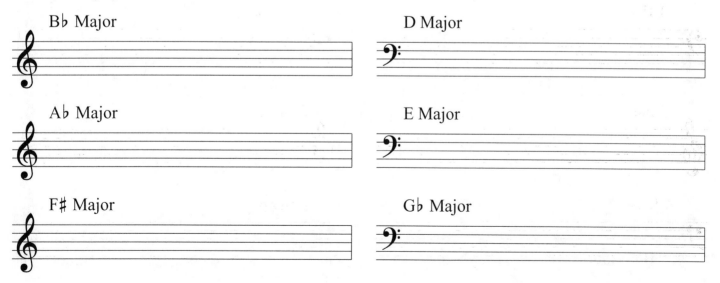

Relative Minor Scales

Each Major scale has a relative minor scale with the same key signature.
The 6th note of the Major scale is the 1st note of the minor scale.

3. Draw the notes of each Major and relative minor scale indicated by the key signature.

_____ Major   _____ minor

_____ Major   _____ minor

_____ Major   _____ minor

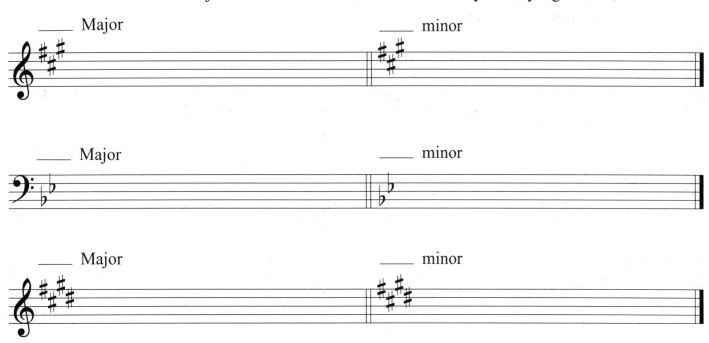

4. Write the key signature indicated, then draw the notes of the minor scale.

1 flat   2 sharps

3 flats   5 sharps

4 flats   1 sharp

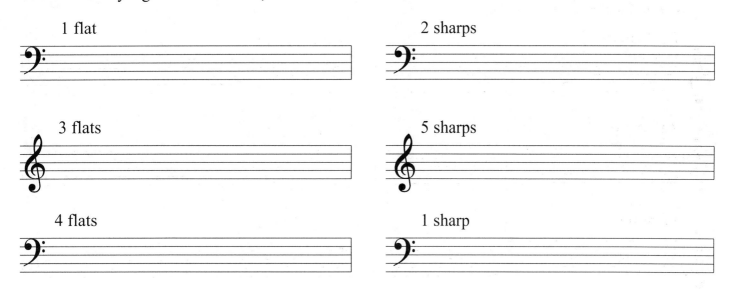

Forms of Minor Scales

There are three forms of minor scales: **natural, harmonic** and **melodic.** The **natural** minor scale follows the key signature exactly: none of the notes are changed. The **harmonic** minor scale has a raised 7th note (1/2 step). The **melodic** minor scale has a raised 6th and 7th note ascending, and then lowered descending. The melodic minor scale descending uses the same notes as the natural minor scale. The altered notes in the harmonic and melodic minor scales must be written in as accidentals.

5. Change these natural minor scales to **harmonic** minor scales by adding the correct accidentals.

C minor

F♯ minor

G minor

6. Change these natural minor scales to **melodic** minor scales by adding the correct accidentals.

C♯ minor

E♭ minor

D♯ minor

Parallel Major and Minor Scales and Keys

Parallel Major and minor scales and keys have the same tonic note. A shift between parallel Major and minor can occur with a change of key signature or with the use of accidentals.

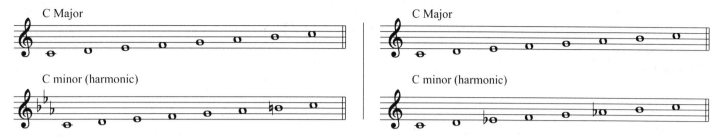

The key signature for the music excerpt below is A minor. A shift between parallel Major and minor occurs with the use of accidentals.

7. Name the scale found in the right hand (treble staff) in measures 103-104. _____

8. Name the scale found in the right hand (treble staff) in measures 107-108. _____

From *Hungarian* by MacDowell
(*Piano Repertoire: Etudes*, Level 9, page 31, measures 101-109)

In the music excerpt below, a shift between parallel Major and minor occurs with a change of key signature.

9. Name the key signature at measure 17. _____

10. Name the key signature after the repeat sign. _____

From *Sonata, Hob. XVI: 37*, by Haydn
(*Piano Repertoire: Baroque & Classical*, Level 9, page 38, measures 17-24)

Unit 4
Intervals

The distance between two notes is called an **interval.**

Interval Qualities

- 2nds, 3rds, 6ths and 7ths may be Major, minor, diminished or Augmented.
- 4ths, 5ths and 8ths (octaves) may be Perfect, diminished or Augmented.

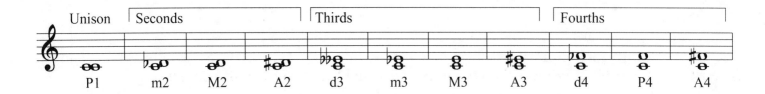

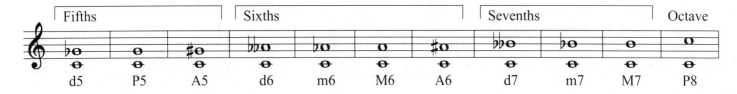

Harmonic and Melodic Intervals

Two notes played together form a **harmonic** interval. Two notes played one at a time form a **melodic** interval.

1. Identify each interval. Write **M** for Major, **m** for minor, **P** for Perfect, **d** for diminished and **A** for Augmented.

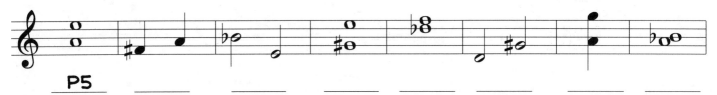

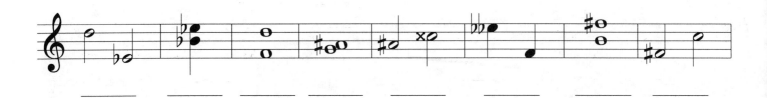

2. Draw one note above the given one to form each interval.

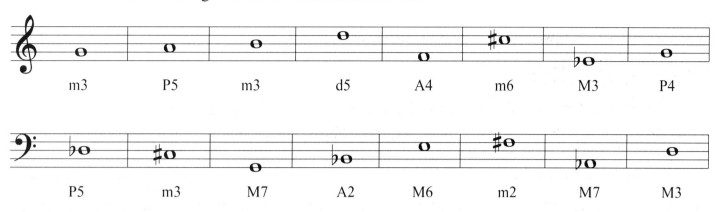

3. Write the name of each interval on the lines above and below these music excerpts.

From *Invention No. 6,* by Bach
(*Piano Repertoire: Baroque & Classical,* Level 9, page 3)

From *Fantasy in D minor* by Mozart
(*Piano Repertoire: Baroque & Classical,* Level 9, page 47)

From *Nocturne in C♯ minor, Op. Post.,* by Chopin
(*Piano Repertoire: Romantic & 20th Century,* Level 9, page 23)

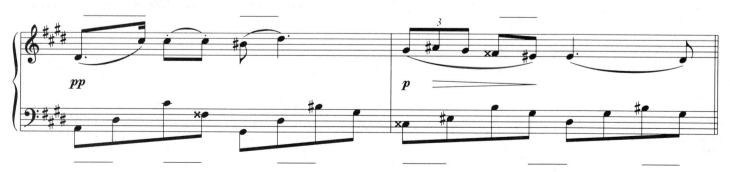

Unit 5
Triads

G Major Triad

A **triad** is a three note chord. The notes of a triad are called the root, 3rd, and 5th. The root names the triad.

Triad Qualities

Triads may be Major, minor, diminished or Augmented. The **Major** triad has a Perfect 5th and a Major 3rd. The **minor** triad has a Perfect 5th and a minor 3rd. The **diminished** triad has a diminished 5th and minor 3rd. The **Augmented** triad has an Augmented 5th and a Major 3rd.

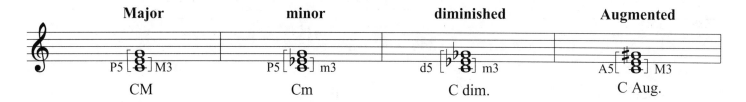

1. Name each triad. Write **M** for Major, **m** for minor, **dim.** for diminished and **Aug.** for Augmented.

F Aug. _____ _____ _____ _____ _____ _____ _____

_____ _____ _____ _____ _____ _____ _____

2. Write these triads.

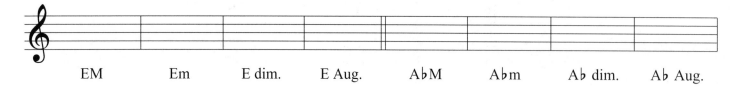

EM   Em   E dim.   E Aug.   A♭M   A♭m   A♭ dim.   A♭ Aug.

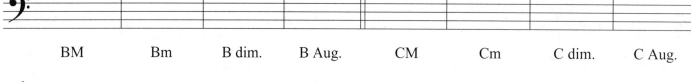

BM   Bm   B dim.   B Aug.   CM   Cm   C dim.   C Aug.

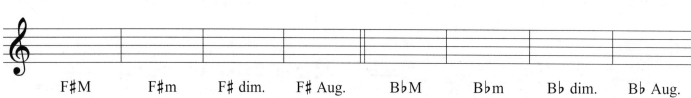

F♯M   F♯m   F♯ dim.   F♯ Aug.   B♭M   B♭m   B♭ dim.   B♭ Aug.

Triads and Inversions

All triads have two **inversions**. A triad is in **root position** when the root of the triad is the lowest note. A triad is in **1st inversion** when the 3rd of the triad is the lowest note. A triad is in **2nd inversion** when the 5th of the triad is the lowest note.

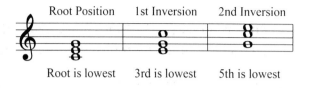

3. Draw the inversions of each root position triad.

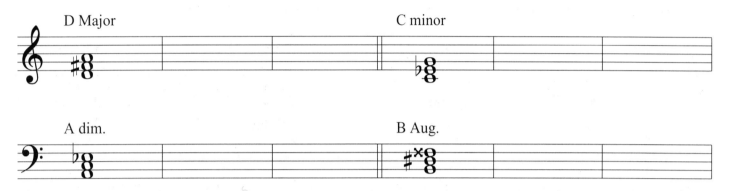

Figured Bass for Triads and Inversions

Figured bass is the use of numbers to identify the inversion of a triad. The figured bass numbers identify the intervals of a triad measured from the bass note (lowest note). The figured bass for a root position triad is $\frac{5}{3}$, however, figured bass is usually omitted for root position triads. The figured bass for a first inversion triad is $\frac{6}{3}$, usually abbreviated to 6. The figured bass for a second inversion triad is $\frac{6}{4}$.

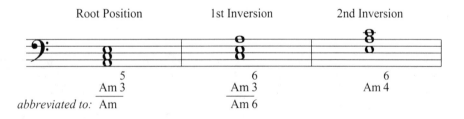

4. Name each triad and write the figured bass.

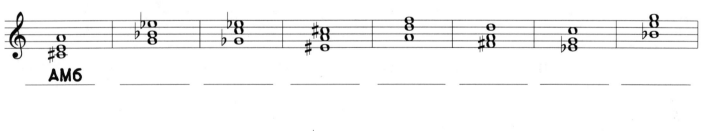

Triads of Major Scales

A triad may be built on each degree of the Major scale. Each triad is labeled with a Roman numeral.

Major = upper case Roman numeral
minor = lower case Roman numeral
diminished = lower case Roman numeral and °

Each triad is named after the scale degree name of its root.

C Major

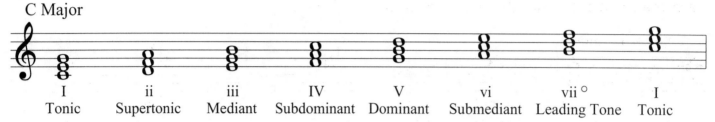

I	ii	iii	IV	V	vi	vii°	I
Tonic	Supertonic	Mediant	Subdominant	Dominant	Submediant	Leading Tone	Tonic

1. Write the Roman numeral and figured bass for each triad of the B Major scale on the lines below the staff. Write the scale degree name for each triad on the lines above the staff.

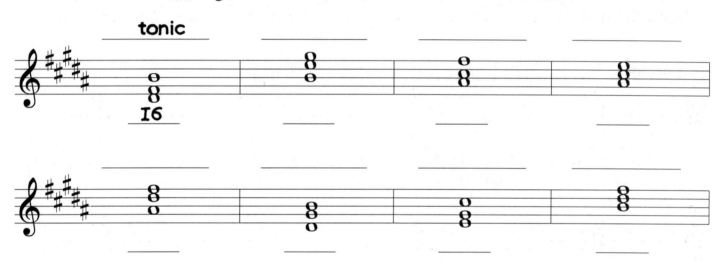

2. Draw each triad of the E♭ Major scale according to the Roman numerals and figured bass. Write the scale degree name for each triad on the lines above the staff.

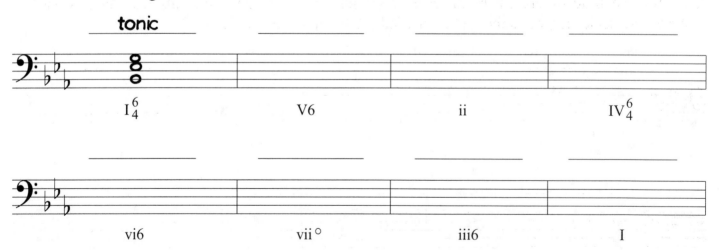

Triads of Minor Scales (Harmonic Form)

A triad may be built on each degree of the minor scale. Each triad is labeled with a Roman numeral.

Major = upper case Roman numeral
minor = lower case Roman numeral
diminished = lower case Roman numeral and °
Augmented = upper case Roman numeral and +

Each triad is named after the scale degree name of its root.

A minor (harmonic)

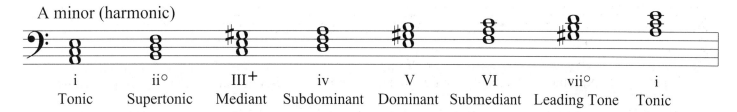

i	ii°	III+	iv	V	VI	vii°	i
Tonic	Supertonic	Mediant	Subdominant	Dominant	Submediant	Leading Tone	Tonic

3. Write the Roman numeral and figured bass for each triad of the G minor scale on the lines below the staff. Write the scale degree name for each triad on the lines above the staff.

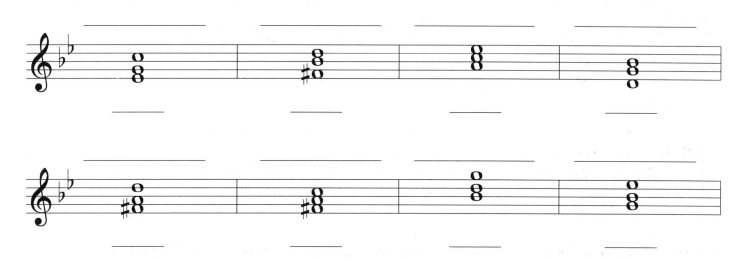

4. Draw each triad of the C♯ minor scale according to the Roman numerals and figured bass. Write the scale degree name for each triad on the lines above the staff.

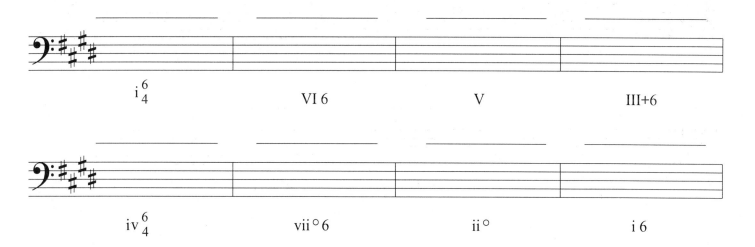

Unit 6
Whole Tone Scale

A **whole tone scale** is made entirely of whole steps. There are only two sets of tones upon which a whole tone scale may be formed. Each set has six tones.

Set 1

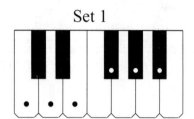

Set 2

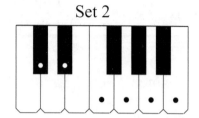

A whole tone scale can begin on any note. The notes can be written with a variety of enharmonic spellings, for example:

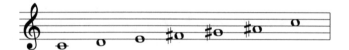

or

1. Draw six notes to complete each whole tone scale.

2. Rewrite each whole tone scale with enharmonic spellings for the notes that are sharp or flat.

Whole Tone Scales in Music

The whole tone scale lacks two of the most important intervals found in Major and minor scales: the Perfect 4th, and Perfect 5th. Due to the fact that it is constructed only with whole steps, the whole tone scale does not have a tonic nor a leading tone and therefore has no inherent feeling of a central or "home" note. The French Impressionist composer Claude Debussy favored the use of the whole tone scale because it represented his rebellion against the use of traditional Major and minor scales. The vague and ambiguous sound of the whole tone scale is appropriate for the Impressionist style, but its usefulness is limited for other styles. After a brief vogue in the first decade of the 20th century, the whole tone scale lost much of its appeal and is rarely used today except for "special effects" in music.

4. Shown below are three music excerpts which are written on whole tone scales. Study each excerpt and determine which set of tones is used in each to form the whole tone scale (set 1 or set 2*). Write your answer on the line above the staff.

From *Voiles* by Debussy

From *Prelude* (Pour le Piano) by Debussy

From *L'isle Joyeuse* by Debussy

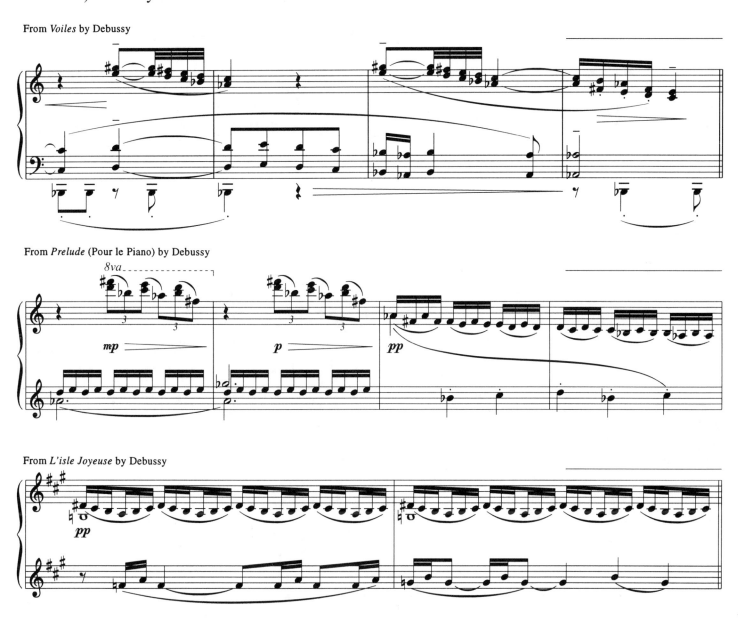

*See page 16.

Unit 7
Seventh Chords

A seventh chord is a four note chord. The notes of a seventh chord are called the root, 3rd, 5th, and 7th.

Seventh Chord Qualities

Five qualities of seventh chords are shown below. These seventh chords are formed with the following combinations of triads and 7ths:

- **Major Seventh Chord**: Major triad plus a Major 7th.
- **Dominant Seventh Chord**: Major triad plus a minor 7th.
- **Minor Seventh Chord**: minor triad plus a minor 7th.
- **Half Diminished Seventh Chord**: diminished triad plus a minor 7th.
- **Diminished Seventh Chord**: diminished triad plus a diminished 7th.

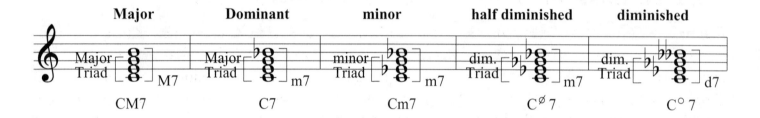

1. Draw Major, Dominant, minor, half diminished and diminished seventh chords on the given roots.

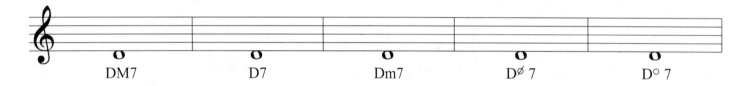

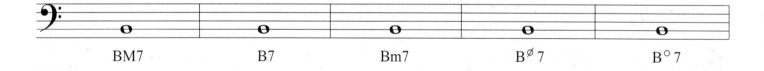

2. Name each seventh chord.

Seventh Chords and Inversions

All seventh chords have three inversions.

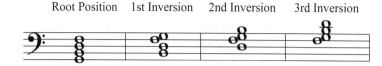

3. Draw the inversions of each root position seventh chord.

Figured Bass for Seventh Chords and Inversions

Figured bass is used to identify the position of a seventh chord. The figured bass numbers identify the intervals of a seventh chord measured from the bass note (lowest note). The figured bass for a root position seventh chord is $\frac{7}{5}$, abbreviated to 7. The figured bass for a 1st inversion seventh chord is $\frac{6}{5}$, abbreviated to $\frac{6}{5}$. The figured bass for 2nd inversion seventh chords is $\frac{6}{4}$, abbreviated to $\frac{4}{3}$. The figured bass for 3rd inversion seventh chords is $\frac{6}{4}$, abbreviated to $\frac{4}{2}$ or 2.

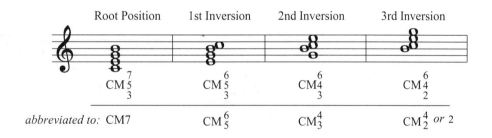

4. Name each seventh chord and write the figured bass.

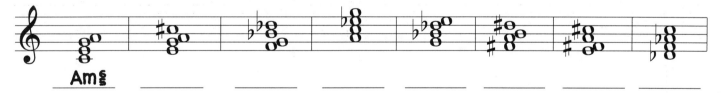

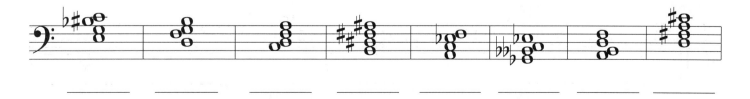

GP669

Seventh Chords of Major Scales

A seventh chord may be built on each degree of the Major scale. Each seventh chord is labeled with a Roman numeral and figured bass. Seventh chords built on the tonic and subdominant notes (I and IV) are Major seventh chords. Seventh chords built on the supertonic, mediant and submediant notes (ii, iii and vi) are minor seventh chords. The seventh chord built on the leading tone (vii) is a half diminished seventh chord. The seventh chord built on the dominant note (V) is the dominant seventh chord.

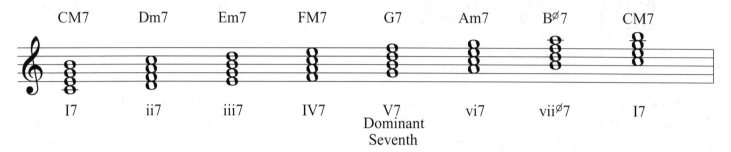

5. Write the Roman numeral and figured bass for each seventh chord of the E Major scale.

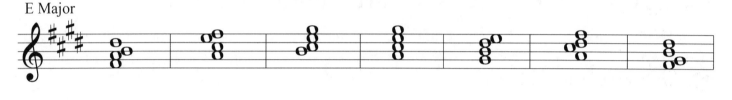

6. Write the Roman numeral and figured bass for each seventh chord of the A♭ Major scale.

7. Draw the dominant seventh chord for each key according to the figured bass.
   (Use the harmonic form for minor keys.)

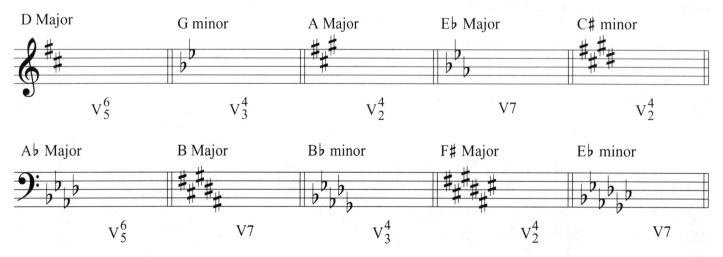

Diminished Seventh Chords

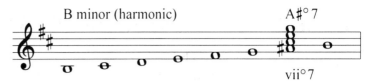

The diminished seventh chord can be built on the leading tone of the harmonic minor scale.

The diminished seventh chord is unique because the root, 3rd, 5th and 7th are all a minor 3rd apart. On the keyboard, the distance between the notes will not change in any inversion. The chords will "feel" the same, but be spelled and written differently.

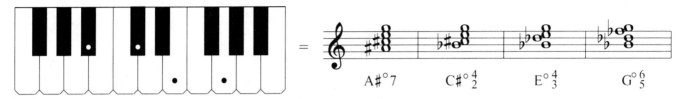

Any note of a diminished seventh chord can become the root by changing the spelling of the chord. Therefore, any note of a diminished seventh chord can become the leading tone of a scale. In the example below, the same diminished seventh chords as in the example above are written in root position. The root of each diminished seventh chord is functioning as a leading tone (vii) resolving to tonic (i).

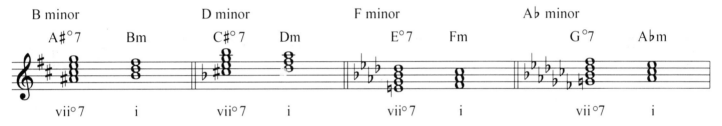

Since any note of a diminished seventh chord can become the root, depending on the spelling of the chord, the diminished seventh chord is frequently used for modulation*. The diminished seventh chord can function like a secondary dominant** (vii°7 of V, vii°7 of IV, etc.). When used in a chord progression, vii°7 of V is usually followed by I_4^6-V7-I, as shown in the music excerpt below.

Although the diminished seventh chord can be built on the leading tone of the harmonic minor scale, diminished seventh chords are used in music in both Major and minor keys. In either a Major or minor key, accidentals must be used when writing a diminished a seventh chord.

From *Sonata, Hob. XVI: 37*, by Haydn
(*Piano Repertoire: Baroque & Classical*, Level 9, page 36)

8. Draw a diminished seventh chord before each given chord according to the figured bass.

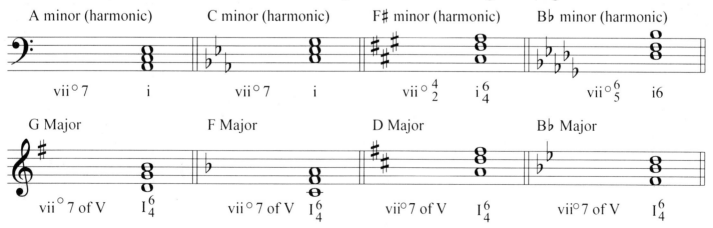

*See Unit 9. **See Unit 7.

Unit 8
Secondary Dominant

A **secondary dominant** is the dominant of a scale degree other than the tonic. Secondary dominants are labeled with Roman numerals designating them as V of ii, V of iii, V7 of IV, etc. Secondary dominants account for most of the accidentals found in music.

1. Play this chord progression which uses secondary dominants in the key of C Major.
   Then, transpose to the keys of B♭ Major and E Major.

2. Write the Roman numerals and figured bass for these chords.

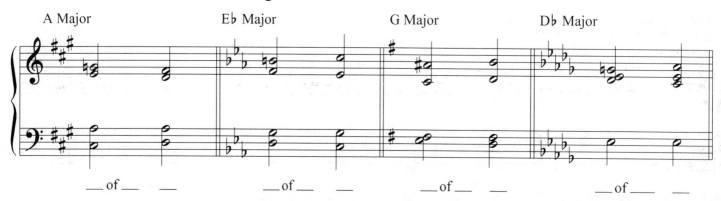

3. Write the Roman numerals and figured bass for each underlined chord in the music excerpts below.

From *Invention No. 6,* by Bach
(*Piano Repertoire: Baroque & Classical,* Level 9, page 3)

E Major

_____   _____ of _____   _____   _____

From *Sonata, Hob. XVI: 37,* by Haydn
(*Piano Repertoire: Baroque & Classical,* Level 9, page 38)

D Major

_____ of _____   _____   _____   _____

From *Sonata, Hob. XVI: 37,* by Haydn
(*Piano Repertoire: Baroque & Classical,* Level 9, page 38)

D Major

_____ of _____   _____   _____ _____

From *Waltz, Op. 64, No. 1,* by Chopin
(*Piano Repertoire: Romantic & 20th Century,* Level 9, page 17)

D♭ Major

_____ of _____   _____   _____   _____

Unit 9
Modulation

Modulation is a change of key within a composition: one key is left and a new one is established. Most modulations occur between keys that are closely related. Closely related keys are those which are adjacent on the circle of keys. The key signatures of closely related keys differ by no more than one sharp or flat. For example, music in the key of C Major frequently modulates to G Major or F Major, or to their relative minor keys of A minor, E minor, or D minor. Recurring accidentals generally indicate a modulation.

Modulation with a Secondary Dominant

Modulation is frequently established with a **secondary dominant.** The secondary dominant becomes the dominant of the new key.

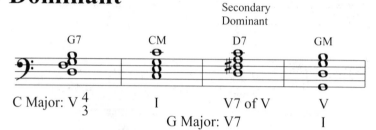

1. The music excerpts below modulate with a secondary dominant. In each music excerpt, write the Roman numerals and figured bass and name the new key.

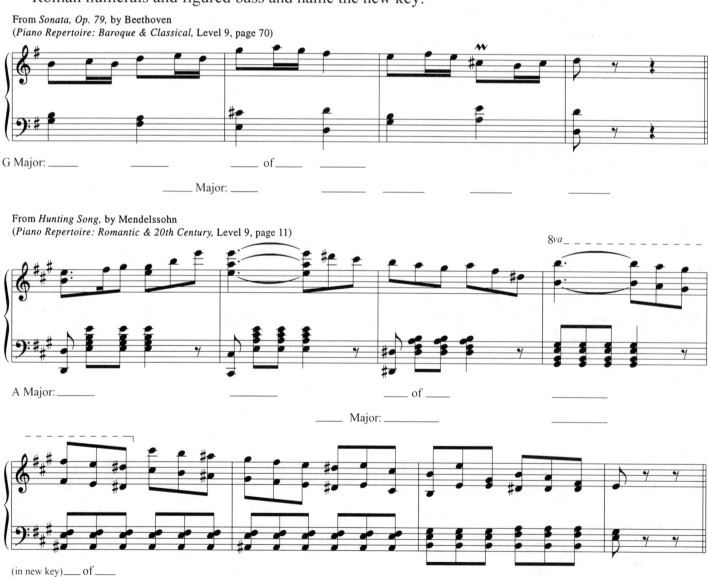

Modulation with a Pivot Chord

Modulation can be established with a chord that exists in both the original key and the new key. This chord is used to **pivot** from the original key to the new key.

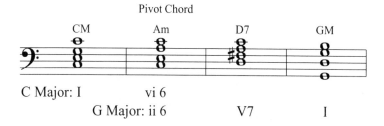

Pivot Chord

CM   Am   D7   GM

C Major: I   vi 6

G Major: ii 6   V7   I

2. The music excerpts below modulate with a pivot chord. In each music excerpt, write the Roman numerals and figured bass and name the new key.

From *Arpeggio Etude,* by Burgmüller
(*Piano Repertoire: Etudes,* Level 9, page 2)

C Major: _____

_____ Major: _____

From *Invention No. 6,* by Bach
(*Piano Repertoire: Baroque & Classical,* Level 9, page 3)

E Major: _____

___ Major: _____

From *Sonata, Op. 79,* by Beethoven
(*Piano Repertoire: Baroque & Classical,* Level 9, page 67)

G minor: _____

_____ Major: _____

Phrase Modulation

Phrase modulation is a sudden change of key. One phrase will cadence in the original key, and the next phrase begins immediately in the new key.

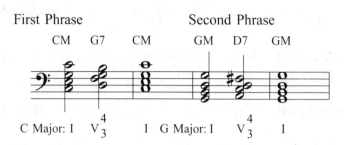

3. The music excerpts below have phrase modulations. Study the music and name the new key for each phrase. Write the Roman numerals and figured bass for the underlined chords.

From *Sonata, Hob. XVI: 37,* by Haydn
(*Piano Repertoire: Baroque & Classical,* Level 9, page 39)

Key of D minor

Key of _____

From *Nocturne in C♯ minor, Op. Post.,* by Chopin
(*Piano Repertoire: Romantic & 20th Century,* Level 9, page 23)

Key of C♯ minor   Key of _____

Key of _____

Unit 10
Cadences

A **cadence** is the combination of two chords used at the end of a phrase, section, or piece of music. The various types of cadences are:

Authentic: V (or V7)-I   **Plagal**: IV-I   **Half**: any cadence ending on V (or V7)   **Deceptive**: V-vi

1. Write the Roman numerals for each chord on the lines under the staff.
   Write the name of each cadence on the line above the staff.

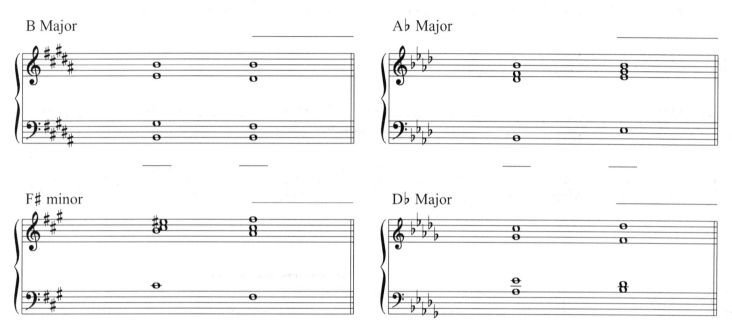

2. Write the Roman numerals for each underlined chord in the music excerpts below.
   Write the name of each cadence on the line above the staff.

From *Sonata, Hob. XVI: 37,* by Haydn
(*Piano Repertoire: Baroque & Classical,* Level 9, page 38)

From *Fantasy* by Mozart
(*Piano Repertoire: Baroque & Classical,* Level 9, page 49)

From *Hunting Song,* by Mendelssohn
(*Piano Repertoire: Romantic & 20th Century,* Level 9, page 10)

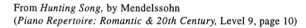

From *Sonata, Op. 79,* by Beethoven
(*Piano Repertoire: Baroque & Classical,* Level 9, page 74)

Unit 11

Chord Progressions:
Modulation to the Dominant

A **chord progression** is a series of chords.
The chord progressions below modulate to the dominant key with a secondary dominant (V7 of V).

C Major: I   V7 of V

    G Major: V7   I   ii6   I$^6_4$ V7   I

G Major: I   V7 of V

    D Major: V7   I   ii6   I$^6_4$ V7   I

1. Write each chord progression according to the Roman numerals and figured bass.

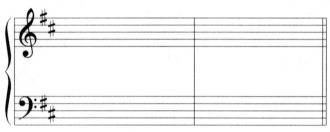

D Major: I   V7 of V

    A Major: V7   I   ii6   I$^6_4$ V7   I

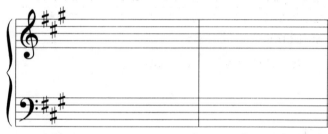

A Major: I   V7 of V

    E Major: V7   I   ii6   I$^6_4$ V7   I

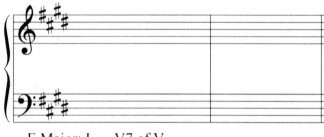

E Major: I   V7 of V

    B Major: V7   I   ii6   I$^6_4$ V7   I

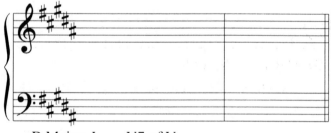

B Major: I   V7 of V

    F♯ Major: V7   I   ii6   I$^6_4$ V7   I

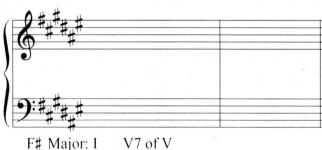

F♯ Major: I   V7 of V

    C♯ Major: V7   I   ii6   I$^6_4$ V7   I

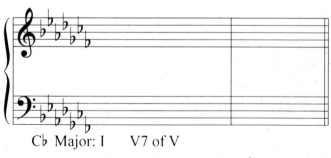

C♭ Major: I   V7 of V

    G♭ Major: V7   I   ii6   I$^6_4$ V7   I

Gb Major: I   V7 of V

Db Major: V7   I   ii6   I$^6_4$ V7   I

Db Major: I   V7 of V

Ab Major: V7   I   ii6   I$^6_4$ V7   I

Ab Major: I   V7 of V

Eb Major: V7   I   ii6   I$^6_4$ V7   I

Eb Major: I   V7 of V

Bb Major: V7   I   ii6   I$^6_4$ V7   I

Bb Major: I   V7 of V

Fb Major: V7   I   ii6   I$^6_4$ V7   I

F Major: I   V7 of V

C Major: V7   I   ii6   I$^6_4$ V7   I

C Major: I   V7 of V

G Major: V7   I   ii6   I$^6_4$ V7   I

G Major: I   V7 of V

D Major: V7   I   ii6   I$^6_4$ V7   I

2. Play each chord progression that you have written. Notice that you are traveling around the Circle
   of Keys as you go from one chord progression to the next.

Unit 12
Fugue

Fugue is the most highly evolved style of imitative polyphonic music from the Baroque Period. It was brought to perfection by J. S. Bach (1685-1750).

Fugue Structure

Although the fugue does not have an exact form, there are basic principles and characteristics in the structure of a fugue. The overall structure of a fugue is the imitation of a subject and a countersubject (or derived motives) in alternating sections called expositions and episodes.

- **Polyphonic Texture:** Fugues are always written in polyphonic texture. Fugues with three or four voices are the most common.

- **Subject:** Fugues are based on a short melody called the subject. The subject is stated at the beginning of the fugue in one voice and is immediately imitated by the other voices. The subject will be stated many times throughout the fugue in all the voices.

- **Answer:** The imitation of the subject in another key, usually the dominant, is called the answer. Answers may be real or tonal. A real answer is an exact transposition of the subject. A tonal answer has modified intervals.

- **Countersubject:** The countersubject is a contrasting melody that is stated in the first voice immediately after the subject as the second voice imitates the subject. The countersubject may be derived from motives in the subject or may be a continuation of the subject. The countersubject will be stated many times throughout the fugue in all the voices.

- **Exposition:** A section in which the subject is stated at least once in each voice is called an exposition. A fugue may have three, four or more expositions. The term exposition is sometimes used only for the first exposition, without any special name for later sections of similar construction. Later expositions usually involve modulations to other keys such as the relative minor, dominant, or subdominant, with a return to the tonic key in the last exposition.

- **Episode:** A section of the fugue which does not include a statement of the subject is called an episode. The exposition sections are separated from one another by episodes. Episodes are usually based on motives from the subject or countersubject. These motives are frequently used in sequences. The episodes, although still in strict polyphonic style, are somewhat freer in structure than expositions.

The Well-Tempered Clavier by J. S. Bach

The Well-Tempered Clavier (Das Wohltemperierte Clavier) is a collection of forty-eight preludes and fugues by J. S. Bach, published in two volumes (1722 and 1744), each of which contains twenty-four preludes and fugues, one for each Major and minor key. The name refers to the then new system of tuning called equal temperament, which made it possible to play equally well in all keys.

The music excerpt below is from a fugue by J. S. Bach. Study the music to answer the questions below.

From *Fugue No. 15, WTC Book 2,* by Bach
(*Piano Repertoire: Baroque & Classical,* Level 9, page 20)

1. In what key is this fugue? _____

2. How many voices are in this fugue? _____

3. Is the answer real or tonal? _____

4. What is the key relationship of the answer to the first statement of the subject? _____

5. In what key does the music cadence at measure 23? _____

6. What is the name for this section of the fugue? _____

Unit 13
Suite

The **suite** is an important form of Baroque keyboard music that consist of a number of movements, each in the character of a dance and all in the same key. The standard scheme of a suite is (1) allemande, (2) courante, (3) sarabande, (4) optional dance or group of dances such as the minuet, bourreé, polonaise and gavotte, (5) gigue. The dance movements are always in binary form.

- **Allemande** (F.): The allemande is in moderate 4/4 time with a short upbeat (usually one sixteenth note). The allemande features continuous sixteenth note passages that are imitated in the various voices creating a basically polyphonic texture. The dance originated from the German *alman.*

- **Bourreé** (F.): The bourreé is a French dance, usually in quick duple meter beginning with a single (one quarter note) upbeat.

- **Corrente** (It.): See Courante.

- **Courante** (F.; It. *corrente, coranto*): The courante is generally characterized by a light texture with rapid figures. The courante became stylized as two types: the French courante and the Italian corrente. The Italian corrente is in quick triple time (usually 3/4) with running passages. The French courante is in a moderate 3/2 or 6/4 time with frequent shifts from one of these meters to the other (see Hemiola, Unit 1, page 2). In most courantes, the change from 3/2 to 6/4 occurs at the final measure of each section.

- **Gavotte** (F.): The gavotte is a French dance in moderate 4/4 time with an upbeat of two quarter notes and phrases generally ending and beginning in the middle of a measure.

- **Gigue** (F.; It. *giga*): The gigue evolved from the Irish or English jig and developed differently in France and in Italy. The French type is characterized by compound meter (usually 6/8), quick tempo, and polyphonic texture of imitative or fugal style. The less common Italian type (giga) is faster (presto), nonfugal, with running passages over a harmonic basis.

- **Minuet** (F. *menuet;* G. *menuett;* It. *minuetto*): The minuet is a French dance in 3/4 time, in moderate tempo. The minuet was the only Baroque dance type that did not become obsolete after the decline of the suite. Two minuets are frequently included in suites to be played in the order of minuet 1 - minuet 2 - minuet 1.

- **Polonaise** (F.): The polonaise is a Polish dance of festive and stately character. The music is always in moderate triple meter, has phrases without upbeat, and generally includes measures with a short repeated rhythmic motive.

- **Sarabande** (F.;Sp. *zarabanda*): The sarabande is a Spanish dance in slow triple meter and dignified style, usually without upbeat and frequently with an accent or prolonged note on the second beat.

1. Study each music excerpt below and determine the correct dance movement name for each.
   Write the dance name on the line above the staff.

2. What is a suite? _____

_____

3. Name, in order, the four standard dance movements in a suite.

(1) _____
(2) _____
(3) _____
(4) _____

3. Name four optional dance movements.

(1) _____
(2) _____
(3) _____
(4) _____

4. What is the form of a dance movement?

_____

5. Match these dance movements with their characteristics.

a. Allemande   ____ Compound meter, quick tempo, imitative

b. Bourreé   ____ French, 3/4 time, moderate tempo

c. Corrente   ____ Spanish, triple meter, slow, accent on second beat

d. Courante   ____ French, upbeat of two quarter notes, phrases ending and beginning in the middle of a measure

e. Gavotte   ____ Polish, triple meter, short repeated rythmic motives

f. Gigue   ____ Italian, usually 3/4 time, running passages

g. Minuet   ____ French, quick duple meter, single upbeat

h. Polonaise   ____ German, moderate 4/4 time, one sixteenth note upbeat, continuous sixteenth note passages

i. Sarabande   ____ French, moderate 3/2 time, shifts to 6/4 at final measures

Unit 14
Toccata

A **toccata** is a style of composition, often very free in form, for keyboard instruments. It originated in the 16th century and remained popular through the Baroque period. Althought the style was largely abandoned during the Classical period, a few composers from the Romantic period and the 20th century wrote toccatas.

The word toccata comes from the Italian word *toccare* which means "to touch". Toccatas are frequently written to display a performer's virtuoso skill, and often focus on one aspect of piano technique such as rapid scales, arpeggios, chords or octaves. As a result, a shorter toccata is usually very unified in motivic and thematic material and often written in a "perpetual motion" style. Longer toccatas may include contrasting sections in a more lyrical style. Toccatas of the Baroque period usually include sections that are imitative or fugal in style.

The music excerpts below are from two different toccatas. The first excerpt is from a toccata by Domencio Paradisi (1707-1791), a Baroque period composer. The second excerpt is from a toccata by James Bastien (1934-), a 20th century composer.

1. Write the Roman numerals and figured bass for each underlined chord in the music excerpt below.

From *Toccata* by Paradisi
(*Piano Repertoire: Baroque & Classical,* Level 9, page 24)

2. Write the chord name for each left hand chord in the music excerpt below.

From *Toccata* by James Bastien
(*Piano Repertoire: Romantic & 20th Century,* Level 9, page 81)

Unit 15
Sonata-Allegro Form

First movements of sonatas are usually written in a form called **sonata-allegro** or *first movement* form*. Sonata-allegro became the most important form of the Classical period and was brought to its highest level of sophistication in the sonatas by Haydn, Mozart and Beethoven.

Sonata-allegro is a ternary form. The three sections of sonata-allegro form are shown below.

1. **Exposition**
   - A. First theme: tonic key
   - B. Second theme: dominant key, or relative Major key if the movement is in a minor key.
   - C. Closing theme (optional): dominant key, or relative Major key if the movement is in a minor key.

2. **Development**

   Themes (and/or motives from themes) are presented in new keys.
   New themes may be added.

3. **Recapitulation**
   - A. First theme: tonic key
   - B. Second theme: tonic key
   - C. Closing theme (optional): tonic key

A **coda** (ending) is sometimes included after the second theme or closing theme.

The relationship of keys is particularly important in sonata-allegro form. In the exposition, the first theme is in the tonic key and the second theme is in the dominant key or in the relative Major key if the movement is in a minor key. In the development, any or all of the themes may be used and they will "travel" through keys other than the tonic, dominant or relative keys. In the recapitulation, both the first and the second theme are in the tonic key. The use of the tonic key for the second theme in the recapitulation gives the music a sound of completion, or of returning "home".

The music on pages 37-41 is the first movement of the Sonata, Hob. XVI:37, by Joseph Haydn (1732-1809). Study the music to answer the following questions.

1. In what key is this piece?　　　　　　　　　　　　　　　_____

2. In what measure does the Exposition and First Theme begin?　　_____

3. Write the Roman numerals for the chords in measure 4 on the lines under the staff.

4. What is the name of the cadence in measure 4?　　　　　　_____

5. Write the Roman numerals for the chords in measure 8 on the lines under the staff.

6. What is the name of the cadence in measure 8?　　　　　　_____

*The term first movement form, although correctly and frequently used, is somewhat misleading because sonata-allegro form is not limited to first movements. Sonata movements other than the first are sometimes written in sonata-allegro form. Sonata-allegro form is also used in symphonies and concertos.

7. Only two chords are formed by the notes in measures 9 and 11.
Write the Roman numerals for these chords. _____ _____

8. What compositional device (such as repetition, sequence, or imitation)
is used in measures 13-14? _____

9. Write the Roman numerals for the chords in measures 15 and 16 on the lines under the staff.

10. What is the name for the cadence in measures 15-16? _____

11. Are there any accidentals in measures 1-16? (yes/no) _____

12. Is there a modulation in measures 1-16? (yes/no) _____

13. In what measure does the Second Theme begin? _____

14. In what key do you expect the Second Theme to be? _____

15. Write Roman numerals and figured bass for the chords in measures 17-23 on the lines under the staff according to the key you named in question 14.

16. Name the Major scale used in measures 22-25. _____

17. Name the compositional device used in measure 20. _____

18. Name the compositional device used in measures 22-25 _____

19. Name the compositional device in measure 27. _____

20. Name the compositional device used in measure 28. _____

21. Compare the music in measure 28 with the music in measure 29.
Which term describes the key relationship of these two measures? (Circle one)   Parallel Relative

22. Name the chord in measure 30. _____

23. Write Roman numerals and figured bass for the chords in measures 32-35 on the lines under the staff according to the key you named in question 14.

24. In what measure does the Closing Theme begin? _____

25. Write Roman numerals and figured bass for the chords in measures 36-40 on the lines under the staff according to the key you named in question 14.

26. In what measure does the Development begin? _____

27. The music is measures 41-46 modulates rapidly through four different keys. Name the key for each measure on the lines under the staff. (Hint: Look for a V7 or vii° chord in each measure to determine the tonic.) Note: The last eighth note of measure 42 should be included in the key of measure 43 rather than measure 42.

28. The music in measure 51-58 stays in one key. This key is also used in measure 43. What is the relationship of this key to the key of the First Theme? (Circle one)

Dominant
Relative Minor

29. Write the Roman numerals and figured bass for the chords in measures 51-58 on the lines under the staff according to the key you named in question 28.

30. Name the chord in measure 55. _____

31. Name the key in measure 59. _____

32. Write the Roman numerals and figured bass for the chords in measure 59 on the lines under the staff according to the key you named in question 31.

33. The chord in measure 60 is V7 in what key? _____

34. In what measure does the Recapitulation begin? _____

35. In what key is the First Theme in the Recapitulation? _____

36. Write Roman numerals and figured bass for the chords in measures 78-79 on the lines under the staff according to the key you named in question 35.

37. In what measure does the Second Theme begin in the Recapitulation? _____

38. In what key do you expect the Second Theme to be in the Recapitulation? _____

39. Write Roman numerals and figured bass for the chords in measure 80-85 on the lines under the staff according to the key you named in question 38.

40. Name the Major scale used in measures 85-88. _____

41. In what measure does the Closing Theme begin in the Recapitulation? _____

42. Write the Roman numerals and figured bass for the chords in measures 95-103 on the lines under the staff according to the key you named in question 38.

43. In this Sonata, there are two chords called **Neapolitan Sixth** chords. A Neapolitan Sixth chord is a Major triad in first inversion, the root of which is a lowered supertonic scale degree. Write the measure numbers in which Neapolitan Sixth chords appear. (Hint: You have already named these two chords in the questions above.)

_____ _____

Sonata

Hob. XVI:37

I.

Joseph Haydn
(1732-1809)

Unit 16
Signs and Terms

Dynamics

TERM	SIGN	MEANING
pianississimo	*ppp*	very, very soft
pianissimo	*pp*	very soft
piano	*p*	soft
mezzo piano	*mp*	medium soft
mezzo forte	*mf*	medium loud
forte	*f*	loud
fortissimo	*ff*	very loud
fortississimo	*fff*	very, very loud
crescendo (cresc.)	<	gradually louder
diminuendo (dim.)	>	gradually softer
fortepiano	*fp*	loud, then immediately soft
sotto voce		in an undertone, subdued

Tempo

TERM	MEANING
adagio	slow
allegro	fast (also means cheerful, happy)
allegretto	somewhat fast (slower than allegro)
andante	walking tempo (flowing)
andantino	slightly faster than andante
animato	animated, with spirit
con moto	with motion
largo	stately, broad, a very slow tempo
lento	slow
moderato	moderately
presto	very fast
vivace	lively, quick
vivo	lively

Changing Tempo

accelerando (accel.)	gradually faster
a tempo	return to the original tempo
allargando	broadening, gradually slower
meno mosso	less motion, slower
piu mosso	more motion, faster
rallentando (rall., rallent.)	gradually slower
ritardando (rit.)	gradually slower
ritenuto	held back, suddenly slower
rubato	freely, flexible; slight accelerandos and ritardandos used for musical expression

Character or Style

TERM	MEANING
cantabile	in a singing manner
con brio	with spirit
con fuoco	with fire
dolce	gently, sweetly
doloroso	sadly, sorrowfully
espressivo	expressively
---etto	little
giocoso	humorous
grazioso	gracefully
--ino	little
leggiero	lightly
meno	less
molto	much, very
pesante	heavily, ponderously
piu	more
poco	little
robusto	boldly, robustly
scherzando	playful
sempre	always
senza	without
simile	in a similar manner, same
smorzando	fading away
spiritoso	spirited
subito	suddenly
tranquillo	peacefully, tranquil, calm

Articulation

TERM	SIGN	MEANING
accent		strong emphasis
legato		smooth, connected
sforzando	*sf* or *sfz*	sudden strong accent
sostenuto		sustained, legato
staccato		short, detached
tenuto		hold full value; slight emphasis

Additional Signs and Terms

Alberti bass: An accompaniment pattern using a three note chord. The notes of the chord are played bottom - top - middle - top.

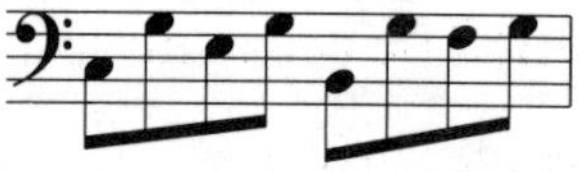

Arpeggio: The notes of a chord played one after another instead of together. The notes of an arpeggio may be written out, or indicated by a wavy line to the left of the chord.

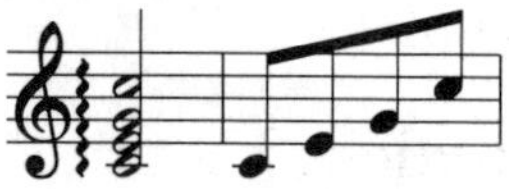

Chromatic Half Step: A half step with two notes of the same letter name (for example: C to C♯).

Diatonic Half Step: A half step with notes of different letter names (for example: C to D♭).

D. C. al Fine (da capo al fine): Play from the beginning to the *fine* (end).

Fermata 𝄐 **:** Hold a note longer than its time value.

Grace Note 𝆕 **:** A grace note is printed in small type. It is not counted in the rhythm; it is played quickly, almost together with the next note.

m.d. (mano destra): Right hand.

m.s. (mano sinistra): Left hand.

Octave Sign *8va*- - - - - - - - -
When the octave sign is placed over notes, play one octave (eight notes) higher than written. When the octave sign is placed under notes, play one octave lower than written.

Opus (Op.): Work. The term is usually used with a number to indicate the chronological order of music written by a composer (Op. 1, Op. 2, Op. 3, etc.).

Pedal Point: A consistent note that is held, repeated, or returned to regularly as harmonies change.

Pedal Sign └──────┘ : The pedal sign shows when to press and lift the damper (right) pedal.

tre corde: Release the soft (left) pedal.

una corda: Depress the soft (left) pedal.

Ornaments

Trill

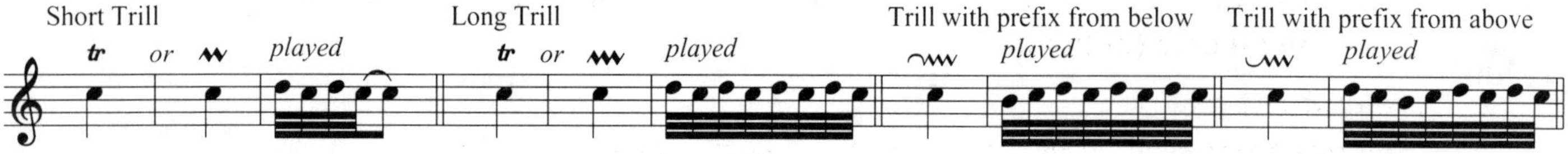

Appoggiatura

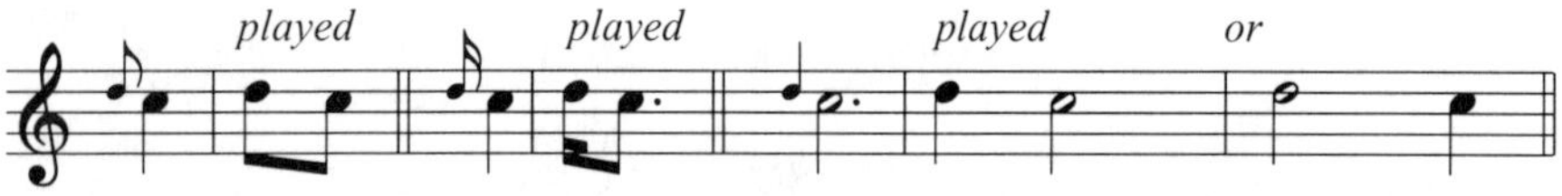

Mordent

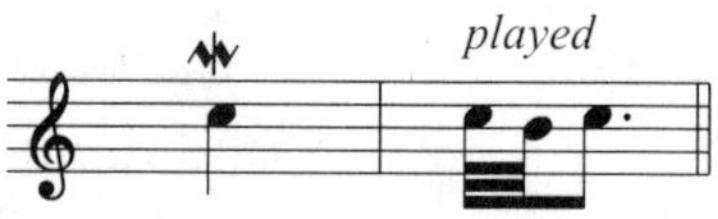

Turn

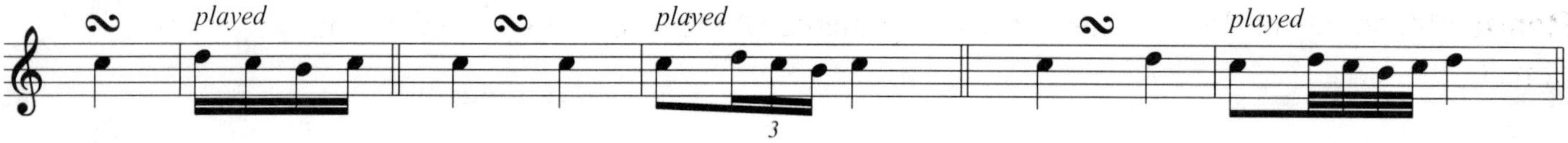

Melodic Phrase Structure

Augmentation: The presentation of a melody or motive with the note values doubled.

Canon: A style of writing in which an extended melody is imitated strictly and entirely in one or more voices.

Diminution: The presentation of a melody or motive with the note values halved.

Imitation: The immediate restatement of a melody or motive in another voice or hand.

Motive (motif): A motive is a short melodic or rhythmic pattern that appears throughout a piece. When the motive appears in the music, it may begin on a different note, the rhythm may change slightly, or the motive may be inverted.

Repetition: Repetition occurs when a melodic or rhythmic pattern is repeated.

Sequence: A sequence occurs when a melodic pattern in repeated at a higher or lower pitch, usually a 2nd or 3rd above or below the original pattern.

Musical Forms

Binary Form: Music in binary form has two sections: section **A** and section **B**. Each section is usually repeated. The **A** section often ends on the dominant note, and the **B** section ends on the tonic.

Ternary form: Music written in ternary form has three sections: section **A,** section **B,** and a repeat of section **A**. The two sections are often contrasting in character or style.

Sonata: The sonata is a composition for piano which has separate sections called movements. The movements are usually contrasting in tempo and character.

Sonatina: The sonatina is a short sonata, usually designed for instruction. A sonatina may have one, two, or three movements. The movements are usually contrasting in tempo and character.

Sonata-Allegro Form: First movements of sonatas and sonatinas are frequently written in a form called "sonata-allegro" or *first movement* form:

    1. **Exposition** section
        A. first theme: tonic key
        B. second theme: dominant key, or relative Major if the piece is in minor key.
        C. closing theme (optional)

    2. **Development** section
        Themes are presented in new keys. New themes may be added.

    3. **Recapitulation** section
        A. first theme: tonic key
        B. second theme: tonic key
        C. closing theme (optional)

Rondo: Music in rondo form has a recurring theme (A) that appears between contrasting sec -tions (B, C, etc.).

Texture in Music

Polyphonic Texture: Music with two or more independent parts or voices (melodies).

Homophonic Texture: Music with melody and accompaniment.

48

1. Write the meaning of each dynamic term.

sotto voce _____   mezzo forte _____

forte piano _____   diminuendo _____

2. Write the meaning of each tempo term.

con moto _____   vivace _____

animato _____   adagio _____

lento _____   presto _____

andante _____   piu mosso _____

accelerando _____   ritenuto _____

rubato _____

3. Write the meaning of each character or style term.

smorzando _____   con fuoco _____

leggiero _____   tranquillo _____

molto _____   cantabile _____

senza _____   meno _____

dolce _____   subito _____

doloroso _____   simile _____

piu _____   poco _____

pesante _____   espressivo _____

4. Write the meaning of each articulation term.

staccato _____   legato _____

sostenuto _____   tenuto _____

accent _____   sforzando _____

5. Define the following terms.

Pedal Point _____

Diatonic Half Step _____

Chromatic Half Step _____

Opus _____

Motive _____

Augmentation _____

Diminution _____

Binary form _____

Ternary form _____

Polyphonic _____

Homophonic _____

m. d. _____   m. s. _____

tre corda _____   una corda _____

6. Write the name of each ornament

𝐭𝐫 or ∿ _____   ♪♩ _____

∾ _____   ∿ _____

7. Match each ornament with its correct performance.

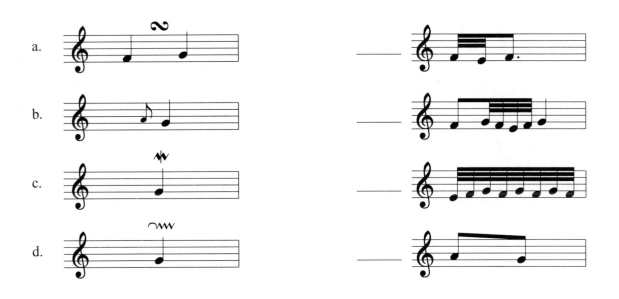

The Four Periods of Music History

The history of music writing is generally divided into four basic periods: (1) Baroque, (2) Classical, (3) Romantic, and (4) 20th Century. Each period has certain styles which make it unique.

1. The Baroque Period (1600-1750)

The era from approximately 1600 to 1750 is known as the Baroque period. The term *baroque* was originally used to describe a style of art and architecture of highly decorative and extravagant design. The aesthetic ideal of the Baroque period permeated all aspects of European culture. Theater, painting, architecture and music were all characterized by grandiose concepts, dazzling effects, ornate design, and an overall dramatic quality.

Historical Context. Important historical events of the Baroque period were the Thirty Years War in Germany (1618-1648), the reign of Louis the XIV of France (1643-1715), the English Civil War (1642-1649), and the Restoration (1660). It was a time of worldwide colonization. Important names in science were Newton and Galileo. The leading philosophers were Descartes and Pascal. Prominent artists of the period include Dutch painters Rembrandt and Van Dyck, and the Spanish painter El Greco. The literature from the period include works by English writers Milton, Defoe, Addison, Swift, and Samuel Johnson, and French writers Racine and Moliere.

Baroque Music. Changes in style and form occurred continuously during the Baroque period, yet certain trends set Baroque music apart from that of other periods.

Basso Continuo. The lowest part in most Baroque music is the *basso continuo* (also called *thoroughbass*). It functions both as a melodic and harmonic bass. The basso continuo part is written in the bass staff with figured bass below the notes. It was the performer's responsibility to fill in the harmony according to the figured bass. This process is called *realizing* the figured bass.

Harmony. Figured bass reflected new harmonic concepts in music. Chords and inversions, authentic cadences, and chromaticism acquired a prominent role. Modulation and the use of seventh chords became commonplace.

Tonality. The Baroque period saw the maturation of the modern concepts of Major and minor tonality. Titles of compositions began to indicate keys (Sonata in D minor, Suite in A Major, etc.) and music began to convey a strong sense of tonal center.

Texture. The texture of Baroque music is predominantly polyphonic. The polyphony is harmonically oriented, and it reached its highest level of mastery in the music of Johann Sebastian Bach. The relative prominence of the bass line is also an aspect of Baroque texture. Homophonic texture exists in certain types of Baroque music where a single melodic line is supported by harmonic material.

Tempo and Dynamics. For the first time in history, some composers began to use tempo and dynamic markings in an attempt to convey the correct expression, emotional content or mood of the music. However, tempo and dynamic markings were limited and not used by all composers.

Improvisation. Improvisation played an important role in the performance of Baroque music. Musicians were highly trained in the art of improvising melodic ornaments, variations on a theme, cadenzas, and the realization of figured bass with complex polyphonic material.

Musical Forms. The most important form that evolved during the Baroque period was the *fugue*. The dance suite was also a prominent form developed during the Baroque period. Dance suite movements were most frequently in binary form. Additional styles of Baroque keyboard pieces include the *invention*, *prelude*, and *toccata*.

Baroque Composers

Bach, Johann Sebastian (Germany, 1685-1750)

Couperin, François (France, 1668-1733)

Daquin, Louis (France, 1694-1772)

Handel, George Frideric (b. Germany 1685-d. England 1759)

Rameau, Jean-Philippe (France, 1683-1764)

Scarlatti, Domenico (b. Italy 1685 - d.Spain 1757)

Telemann, Georg Philipp (Germany, 1681-1767)

Baroque Keyboard Instruments. Precursors of the modern piano are the *clavichord* and *harpsichord*. The clavichord mechanism produced a tone by means of a small metal tangent attached to the end of the key which struck the strings from below. The tone was delicate and the instrument was used mostly in intimate settings. The harpsichord became the "concert grand" of the 18th century. The tone of this plucked keyboard instrument was fuller and had more carrying power than that of the clavichord. An early version of the harpsichord was constructed in 1503 by Giovanni Spinetti of Venice. Named after its inventor, the *spinet* (called the *virginal* in England) produced a tone by plucking the string with a quill. In France, the harpsichord was called the *clavecin*, and in Italy, the *cembalo* or *clavicembalo*. Later harpsichord makers added longer strings and various stops and pedals. By the mid-17th century harpsichords had two keyboards, with two or three strings for each pitch to produce a fuller tone.

Baroque composers adapted their compositions to the capabilities of the clavichord and harpsichord. Since the harpsichord was unable to produce gradual tone gradations (crescendos and diminuendos), composers wrote "echo" effects: a phrase played loud on one keyboard and then repeated softly on a second keyboard. The juxtaposition of loud and soft dynamics is called *terraced dynamics*. Because of the lack of sustaining power, especially of the harpsichord, numerous embellishments were added to "fill-in" the sound. Through the use of various stops and coupling or dampening of the strings a variety of effects could be made.

2. The Classical Period (1750-1825)

The 18th century encompasses several stylistic trends which overlap chronologically. It includes the diverse musical concepts of style and form of the late Baroque, Pre-Classical, and Classical periods. The years from 1750 to 1825 represent the rise and culmination of classicism in music.

Historical Context. The years from 1750 to 1825 were marked by the rise of democratic forces manifested in the French Revolution. Other military conflicts were the Seven Years' War (1756-1763), the French and Indian Wars in America, the conflict between England and the American colonies culminating in the Declaration of Independence (1776) and the American Revolution, the War of 1812, and the Napoleonic Wars in Europe. Important writers of the time include Voltaire and Rousseau. Artists of the period include Watteau, Goya, David, Gainsborough, and Copley. Achievements in science were the development of the first vaccine, the discoveries of oxygen, hydrogen, electromagnetic induction, and ultraviolet rays. The invention of the steam engine, cotton gin, electric motors and generators were factors in the Industrial Revolution, which began in England around 1760.

Pre-Classical Music. Music which represents the transition from the Baroque to Classical period is usually called Pre-Classical. Changes in concepts of form and style took place from approximately 1720 to 1750. No clear line of separation can be drawn between late Baroque, Pre-classical and early Classical music. A variety of styles often occur in works of the same composer. Basic changes include the abandonment of polyphonic texture in favor of homophonic texture, the disappearance of the basso continuo, and binary form replaced with ternary form.

Pre-Classical Composers

Bach, Johann Christian (Germany, 1735-1782)
Bach, Carl Philipp Emanuel (Germany, 1714-1788)
Bach, Wilhelm Friedemann (Germany, 1710-1784)
Benda, Georg (Germany, 1722-1795)

Kirnberger, Johann Philipp (Germany, 1721-1783)
Mozart, Leopold (Austria, 1719-1787)
Paradisi, Domenico (Italy, 1707-1791)

Classical Music. The word *classical* may be defined with three contrasting meanings: (1) the art and literature of ancient Greece, (2) the antonym of "popular" music, and (3) the era from approximately 1750 to 1825. It is the third definition that is used in music history. Classicism implies the ideals of the Apollonian cult of ancient Greece: objectivity, ethos, emotional restraint, and the balance and clarity of form. These ideals are reflected in the music of the Classical period.

Form. Ternary forms, particularly sonata-allegro form, were firmly established during the Classical period. Phrase structure was characteristically clear with well defined cadences, and phrases were shorter (usually four measures) than in Baroque music.

Texture. Classical music was usually in homophonic texture, often a single melodic line with accompaniment. The most typical accompaniment pattern was the *Alberti bass*, named for the Pre-Classical composer Domenico Alberti (1710-1740). Polyphonic texture did not disappear completely, however fugues and other polyphonic forms were rarely written. Another aspect of Classical texture was the prevalence of thin, light sonorities as opposed to the predominantly massive sounds of Baroque music.

Melodic Style. Classical melodies were more concise with more thematic unity than the long, continuous lines of Baroque music. Classical melodies were generally diatonic.

Harmony. Classical harmony was overall less complex than Baroque harmony. More emphasis was given to primary triads, and diatonic harmony was more typical than chromatic. Chords were usually triadic, and seventh chords were used sparingly.

Improvisation. The art of improvisation died out with the disappearance of the basso continuo. All harmony was written out. Composers became more specific and consistent with the indications of ornamentation, phrasing, dynamics, and other details formerly left to the discretion of the performer.

Absolute Music. The classical period favored what is called *absolute music*: music which does not attempt to describe extra-musical things nor include descriptive titles.

Classical Composers.

Beethoven, Ludwig van (Germany, 1770-1827)   Kuhlau, Friedrich (b. Germany 1786 - d. Denmark 1832)

Clementi, Muzio (b. Italy 1752 - d. England 1832)   Mozart, Wolfgang Amadeus (Austria, 1756-1791)

Czerny, Carl (Austria, 1791-1857)   Pleyel, Ignaz (France, 1757-1831)

Haydn, Joseph (Austria, 1732-1809)   Türk, Daniel Gottlob (Germany, 1756-1832)

Classical Period Pianos. The possibilities of combining the sustaining tone of the clavichord with the power of the harpsichord were no doubt alluring to musicians and keyboard builders of the 17th century. It is not surprising that three inventors working independently in different countries perceived the hammer action piano concept at about the same time: Cristofori in Italy (1709), Marius in France (1716), and Schroter in Germany (1717). Credit is given to Bartolomeo Cristofori, curator of musical instruments for the wealthy Medici family in Florence, for producing the first piano. Cristofori called his invention a *gravicembalo col piano e forte* (a keyboard instrument which can play soft and loud). The ability of the early piano to produce graded dynamics (crescendos and diminuendos), plus its sustaining quality appealed to composers and keyboard makers of the time. By about 1728, Cristofori had improved his pianoforte by constructing a much stronger case than had been used for harpsichords to withstand the increased strain of heavier strings. The action at this time resembled the basic mechanics of the modern piano: escapement device, a back check regulating the fall of the hammer, and a damper for each key. Pianoforte building was continued by craftsmen such as Gottfried Silbermann, and his pupils Johannes Zumpe and Americus Becker who went to London to establish English pianoforte building. One of Silbermann's most talented pupils, Johann Stein, carried Viennese pianoforte making to new heights, and his instruments were preferred by Mozart, Beethoven, and others. The early pianos were small and produced a light, delicate sound. Mozart's piano had a range of not quite five octaves. A piano built by Broadwood in 1817 for Beethoven had a range of six octaves. It is interesting to note that J. S. Bach played one of Silbermann's pianos, and although he praised its tone, he complained that it was too weak in the treble, and it was too hard to play (stiff action).

3. The Romantic Period (1825-1900)

The period of time from about 1825 to 1900 is known as the Romantic period. However, aspects of romanticism appeared before 1825 and continued well into the 20th century.

Historical Context. Progress in science and engineering (photography, the railway and steamboat, steel production, electricity, the telephone and telegraph, and other innovations) influenced the cultural, economic, political, and social orders of the 19th century. The growth of technology expanded the Industrial Revolution in Europe and created new social and economic dilemmas: the development of capitalism and the appearance of socialism. 19th century conflicts included the Crimean War (1854-1856), the Civil War in the United States (1861-1865), and the Franco-Prussian War (1870-1871). The most important movement in art was French Impressionism in the second half of the century, represented by Manet, Degas, Monet and Renoir. Related to this movement were the French symbolist poets Verlaine, Mallarmé, and Rimbaud. Prominent philosophers of the period included Hegel and Nietzsche. It was the era of great Romantic literature: Byron, Wordsworth, Dickens, Keats, Schiller, Goethe, Heine, E. T. A. Hoffmann, Lamartine, Hugo, Flaubert, Emerson, Poe, Mark Twain, and many others.

Romantic Music. Romanticism, perceived as the antonym of classicism, implies the Dionysian ideals of ancient Greece: pathos, subjectivity, emotionalism, placing instinct over reason and sentiment over precise form. The 19th century was a time characterized by the desire for individualism and nationalism. Composers of the Romantic period became more socially and economically independent, no longer relying on the patronage of the church or aristocracy. Music was generally composed for one of two settings: the concert hall or the more intimate salon. There were notable extremes in length of compositions: extensive works (concertos, symphonies, operas) and shorter works (songs and piano pieces). Composers developed a greater affinity with poetry, literature, and art, and as a result favored more descriptive or "programmatic" music. The virtuoso concert performer became a much admired musician, and virtuosity in music developed into a common trait. The Romantic period is a particularly rich era for pianists because it significantly expanded the amount of repertoire for the piano. Nationalism also became a notable trend. Composers deliberately incorporated national styles by using folklore as subjects for operas, songs, and programmatic music, often using folk tunes and folk styles in their compositions.

Melody. Melodies in Romantic music generally have qualities of personal warmth and expressiveness, a more lyrical style, and more flexible phrase structure.

Harmony. The harmonic language of the Romantic period became an important means for expression through expanded chord structure and progressions. Chromaticism and modulation played important roles, along with a freer treatment of dissonance and the frequent appearance of seventh chords.

Tonality. Music of the Romantic period was still tonal (in a central key). However, the feeling of being in a key was frequently obscured by extended chromatic modulations to unrelated keys. This trend paved the way for radically new concepts of tonality in the 20th century.

Texture. Music of the Romantic period was primarily in homophonic texture yet included frequent use of secondary melodies and/or polyphonic techniques. The sonority of Romantic music was notable for a marked increase in the richness of sound.

Dynamics. Composers of the Romantic period exploited the inherent possibilities of dynamics for emotional expression. It became characteristic of the period to use a wide range of dynamic levels between loud and soft and extensive use of crescendo and diminuendo.

Form. Content and subjective expression became more important than strict musical form. As a result, forms such as binary, ternary, sonata-allegro, rondo, etc., were generally freer, more variable, and often less distinct than in the Classical period. Short piano pieces were often given descriptive titles and are called *character pieces*. They include pieces with such titles as *arabesque, ballad, intermezzo, nocturne, rhapsody, impromptu, bagatelle, songs without words*, and descriptive titles such as *Venetian Boat Song, Butterfly, March of the Dwarfs*, etc. Stylized dances such as the *waltz, mazurka*, and *polonaise* became a significant portion of the piano repertoire. The *etude*, basically a study featuring some technical aspect of performance (scales, arpeggios, octave, chords, etc.) was composed as a virtuoso piece for concert audiences.

Romantic Composers.

Brahms, Johannes (Germany, 1833-1897)
Burgmüller, Friedrich (b. Germany 1806-d. France 1874)
Heller, Stephan (Germany, 1814-1888)
Chopin, Frédéric (b. Poland 1810- d. France 1849)
Grieg, Edvard (Norway, 1843-1907)
Liszt, Franz (Hungary, 1811-1886)
Mendelssohn, Felix (Germany, 1809-1847)
Schubert, Franz (Austria, 1797-1828)
Schumann, Robert (Germany, 1810-1856)
Spindler, Fritz (Germany, 1817-1905)
Streabbog, Jean Louis (France, 1835-1886)
Tchaikovsky, Peter Ilyich (Russia, 1840-1893)

Romantic Period Pianos. The period of 1760 to 1830 was one of great activity in the development of the piano. The French piano builders Sebastien and Erard developed an instrument with greater tone using a larger sound board (1776-1777). Because of the piano's capacity for sonority, dynamic range, and gradations between loud and soft, it became the Romantic instrument of choice. It provided composers and performers with possibilities of emotional expression ranging from intimate to grandiose, from delicate lyricism to bombastic showiness. The damper pedal enabled composers to experiment with new harmonic effects, and the improved keyboard mechanism stimulated new idioms, technics, and virtuosity.

4. The 20th Century (1900-2000)

The 20th century is an era in which the rapidity and significance of changes are unparalleled in history. Events and developments in political, social, scientific, and cultural history profoundly influenced the course of music.

Historical Context. Two global wars in the first half of the 20th century had powerful impacts on world history: World War I (1914-1918) and World War II (1939-1945). Each conflict was followed by an effort to establish world government: the League of Nations (1920-46) and the United Nations (established in 1946). The Bolshevik Revolution in 1917 marked the emergence of Communism and of Russia as a world power. Conflicts since the mid-century were the Korean War (1950-1953), the Arab-Israeli conflict, and the Vietnam wars. A political and ideological struggle between the Soviet Union and the United States after World War II was known as the Cold War, a period of nonmilitary activity, but one marked by a major armaments race.

Tremendous advances in science and engineering and their application to industry affected social, economic, and cultural history. Extensive progress took place in biology, chemistry, physics, and astronomy. Remarkable developments in technology were made in the areas of communication, transportation, and medicine. Some specific innovations include radio, television, atomic energy, jet propulsion, computers, antibiotics, exploration of space and of suboceanic areas, and, especially relevant to music, high-fidelity sound transmission.

As with all periods in history, the spirit of the times is reflected in the arts. 20th century trends include frequent and rapid changes, and experimentation with new forms. A general trend away from realism and toward abstract and subjective expression is particularly apparent in the visual arts. Important trends in art include expressionism, cubism, surrealism, pop art, minimal art, and conceptual art. Styles in literature, poetry, and theater also reflect the era: social protest, existentialism, pessimism and despair, absurdity, and intentional "shock value" are distinct traits.

20th Century Music. From a historical point of view, the study of 20th century music poses a number of problems not encountered in previous periods. So far, no satisfactory name has been devised (comparable with Baroque, Classical, or Romantic) for 20th century music. The expression "contemporary period" is frequently used, yet is rather misleading since it implies that which is current, as opposed to that which was heard in previous decades of the 20th century. The expression "modern music" is also frequently used, but its implications are so variable that it is almost meaningless. Due to the enormous quantity of music written since 1900, the extraordinary diversity of trends, styles and technics, and the rapidity and frequency of change, it is difficult to perceive and evaluate 20th century music as a coordinated whole. Unlike previous periods, no single style represents the 20th century, or even a appreciable portion of it. The elements of melody, harmony, tonality, texture, rhythm, and form are so complex and varied in 20th century music that they virtually preclude the systematic analysis that can be applied to the music of previous periods.

Several important styles emerged among the diversity of music in the 20th century. Some styles are more prominent than others, and some of longer duration than others. The various styles of 20th century music frequently overlap in their development and are not necessarily in chronological order. Also, they are often not distinctly separate developments. The unique character of one composer may be a composite of more than one style. Several of the important styles are Late Romanticism, Impressionism, Neo-Classicism, and Jazz.

Late Romantic Music. While revolutionary new styles were appearing in the early decades of the 20th century, trends of the Romantic period prevailed. Subjectivity, emotionalism, and programmatic music were traits that remained even in compositions which used new harmonies, rhythms, and tonalities.

Late Romantic Composers

Ernst von Dohnanyi (Hungary, 1877-1960)	Edward MacDowell (USA, 1860-1908)
Anatol Liadov (Russia, 1855-1914)	Sergei Rachmaninoff (Russia, 1873-1943)

Impressionist Music. Impressionism, often referred to as a "transitional period", was the first important trend leading to the changing styles of the 20th century. It paralleled the French movements in painting and poetry, and was largely a reaction against the Romantic period. Although Impressionism shares some common traits with Romantic music (it is generally subjective and programmatic), it abandoned traditional compositional technics in several ways. It may be described as having a high degree of delicacy, vagueness of form, and generally a "luminous fog" atmosphere. Specific technics include the use of open chords (5ths and octaves without 3rds), parallel chords and other unconventional chord progressions, whole tone scales, and freer treatment of meter.

Impressionist Composers.

Claude Debussy (France, 1862-1918)	Maurice Ravel (France, 1875-1937)
Francis Poulenc (France, 1899-1963)	Eric Satie (France, 1866-1925)

Neo-Classical Music. Neo-classicism is one of the most prominent and prevailing styles in music of the 20th century. It appeared about 1920, and continues through the entire century. Neo-classical music uses pre-romantic period ideals of objectivity, and clarity of form. It also revives polyphonic textures and forms of the Baroque period (fugue, toccata, etc.) while using 20th century concepts of harmony, melody, tonality, and rhythm.

Neo-Classical Composers

Paul Hindemith (Germany, 1895-1963)	Gian Carlo Menotti (Italy, 1911-)
Norman Dello Joio (USA, 1913-)	Sergei Prokofiev (Russia, 1891-1953)
Dmitri Kabalevsky (Russia, 1904-1987)	Igor Stravinsky (Russia, 1882-1971)
Aram Khachaturian (Russia, 1903-1978)	Alexander Tcherepnin (Russia, 1899-1977)

Jazz. Particularly a 20th century phenomenon, and primarily an American innovation in popular music, Jazz is an important style which has influenced many trends of serious composition. In its broadest definition, Jazz is improvised instrumental dance music. However, the variety of Jazz styles preclude summation in one concise category. The various types of Jazz include *Ragtime, Blues, Dixieland, Big Band, Swing, Boogie-Woogie, Bop, Progressive Jazz, Cool Jazz, Third-Stream,* and *Rock and Roll*. As well as influencing the myriad of trends of popular music of the 20th century, many "classical" composers have incorporated Jazz elements into their music.

20th Century Compositional Techniques. In addition to the various new styles of music discussed above, there are significant changes in compositional techniques in music of the 20th century. These changes are evident primarily in the elements of rhythm, melody, harmony, and tonality. However, it should be understood that not all music of the 20th century is a reflection of radical change in all respects. Any 20th century composition may have one or two elements that reflect 20th century technics, and not necessarily to the extreme. The music of the 20th century ranges from ultra-conservative to avant-garde, most of which lies somewhere between the two extremes.

Meter and Rhythm. Composers of the 20th century sought new metric and rhythmic effects. In general, rhythm is used with more complexity, variety, and flexibility. Odd-numbered time signatures such as $\frac{5}{4}$ and $\frac{7}{8}$ are commonly found. Asymmetrical groupings of beats are used to create rhythmic effects. For example, in $\frac{7}{8}$, beats may be felt in patterns such as 3-2-2 or 2-2-3. Occasionaly, the time signature may be written as $\mathbf{2+\frac{2}{8}+3}$. In a more dramatic attempt at rhythmic flexibility, some composers omitted bar lines altogether.

Melody. Although many melodies in 20th century music are conservative, certain melodic characteristics are distinctly 20th century innovations. More extreme melodic styles include *disjunct melodies* (wide leaps from one note to the next), *angularity* (alternating upward and downward direction), and the use of dissonant intervals. Unconventional scales such as the *whole tone scale, pentatonic scale,* and *modal scales* also contribute to 20th century melodic styles.

Harmony. No element of 20th century music manifests more radical change than harmony. The tertian construction of chords (chords built with intervals of 3rds), such as triads and seventh chords, was augmented with the addition of more 3rds, resulting in 9th, 11th, and 13th chords. New types of 20th century chord construction include *quartal harmony* (chords built in 4ths), *tone clusters* and *polychords* (two or more different chords used simultaneously). Traditional chord progressions are largely abandoned in 20th century music and often replaced with arbitrary progressions, frequently involving chords with roots not related to the key. 20th century harmonic effects are often created with simple triads moving in parallel motion. One of the most distinct characteristics of 20th century harmony is the extent and degree to which dissonance is used. Unlike conventional harmony of the Baroque, Classical and Romantic periods, resolution of dissonance is not a prerequisite.

Tonality. Towards the end of the Romantic period, tonality (the feeling of being in a key, or gravitating towards a tonic note) was often obscured with increased chromaticism and prolonged modulations. Music of the 20th century departs further from traditional tonal concepts. 20th century innovations include *bitonality* (the use of two keys at the same time) and *polytonality* (the use of three or more keys at the same time) and *atonality* (the absence of any tonal center or key feeling). New scale constructions and the prolonged used of dissonance also contribute to tonal ambiguity.

Serialism. Serial music is constructed on the basis of a recurrent series of notes, rhythms, dynamics or other elements. Serialism first appeared in the 1920's with the development of the *twelve-tone row*. Serialism is related to both atonality and new concepts of form and structure in music.

20th Century Composers. Although names of composers were included in the preceding discussions of the various 20th century musical styles, many 20th century composers use a variety of styles and techniques and defy exact categorization. Listed here are a number of significant composers not named in the aforementioned text.

Agay, Denes (USA, 1911-)	Ginastera, Alberto (Argentina, 1916-1983)
Barber, Samuel (USA, 1910-1981)	Muczynski, Robert (USA, 1929 -)
Bartók, Béla (b. Hungary 1881 d. New York 1945)	Pinto, Octavio (Brazil, 1890-1950)
Bastien, James (USA, 1934-)	Rocherolle, Eugénie (USA, 1936-)
Britten, Benjamin (England, 1913-1976)	Shostakovich, Dmitri (Russia, 1906-1975)
Copland, Aaron (America, 1900-1990)	Tansman, Alexander (B. Poland 1897, d. France 1986)
Gershwin, George (USA 1898-1937)	Turina, Joaquin (Spain, 1882-1949)
Gillock, Willian (USA, 1917-1996)	Villa-Lobos, Heitor (Brazil, 1887-1959)

Unit 18
Ear Training

Practice #1

Listen as your teacher plays one interval from each pair. Circle the one you hear.

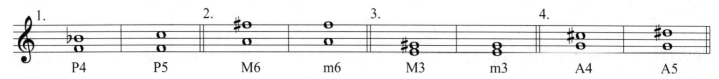

Listen as your teacher plays one triad from each pair. Circle the one you hear.

Listen as your teacher plays a triad in 1st inversion ($\frac{6}{3}$) or 2nd inversion ($\frac{6}{4}$). Circle the one you hear.

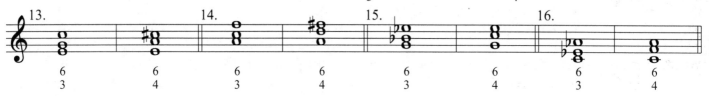

Listen as your teacher plays one seventh chord from each pair. Circle the one you hear.

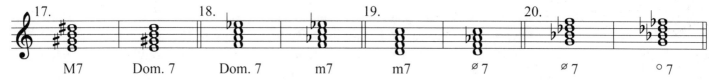

21. Listen as your teacher plays one of the scales below. Check (✓) the one you hear.

22. Listen as your teacher plays one of the melodies below. Check (✓) the rhythm that you hear.

Practice #2

Listen as your teacher plays one interval from each pair. Circle the one you hear.

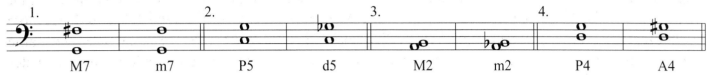

Listen as your teacher plays one triad from each pair. Circle the one you hear.

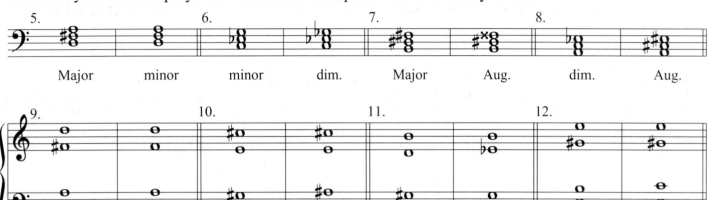

Listen as your teacher plays a triad in 1st inversion ($\frac{6}{3}$) or 2nd inversion ($\frac{6}{4}$). Circle the one you hear.

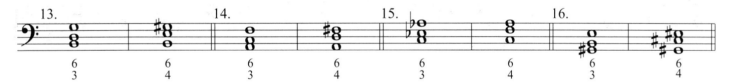

Listen as your teacher plays one seventh chord from each pair. Circle the one you hear.

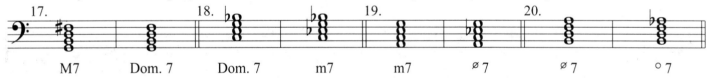

21. Listen as your teacher plays one of the scales below. Check (✔) the one you hear.

_____ Natural   _____ Harmonic   _____ Melodic

22. Listen as your teacher plays one of the melodies below. Check (✔) the rhythm that you hear.

Unit 19
Sight Reading

The best way to become a good sight reader is to read new music every day.

1. Before you sight read, look through the entire piece and observe:
   - the key signature
   - the time signature
   - the clef signs
   - dynamics
   - accidentals
   - slurs, ties, staccatos, accents, etc.
   - rhythmic and melodic patterns

2. Find the first note and finger number for each hand.

3. Play slowly.
   - Use a metronome to keep a steady beat.
   - Count one measure aloud before you begin to play.
   - Continue to count aloud as you play.

4. Keep your eyes on the music.
   - Avoid looking up and down from the music to your hands.
   - Look ahead to see what is next.

5. Keep going, even if you make some mistakes; avoid going back to "fix" anything.

6. After you sight read, evaluate your playing.
   - Were the notes and rhythm correct?
   - Were the dynamics and articulation markings clear and distinct?
   - Did the music continue to move forward as you maintained a steady beat?

7. Sight read the music again.
   - Concentrate on correcting any previous mistakes.
   - Set a goal for a perfect performance by the third reading.

Bourreé

Sarabande

Gigue

Review Test

1. Study this rhythm to answer the questions below.

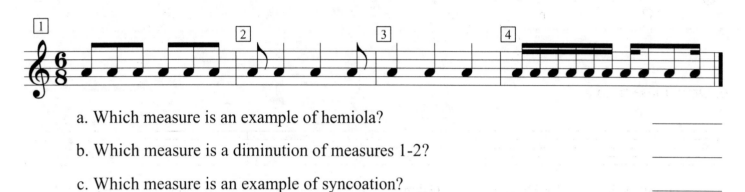

    a. Which measure is an example of hemiola? _____

    b. Which measure is a diminution of measures 1-2? _____

    c. Which measure is an example of syncoation? _____

2. Write these key signatures.

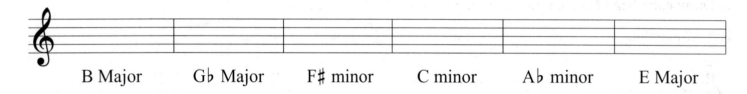

    B Major   Gb Major   F# minor   C minor   Ab minor   E Major

3. Draw these scales one octave, ascending.

    A Major   E harmonic minor

    Eb Major   Whole tone, beginning on Gb

4. Add the correct accidentals to form the F melodic minor scale.

5. Draw one note above the one given to form each interval.

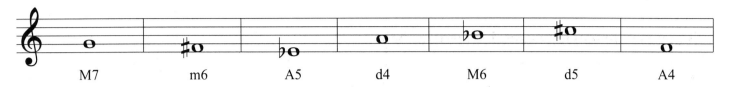

M7   m6   A5   d4   M6   d5   A4

6. Draw these triads.

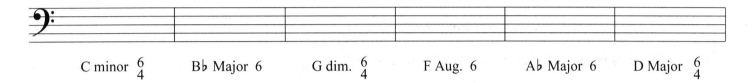

C minor $\begin{smallmatrix}6\\4\end{smallmatrix}$ B♭ Major 6   G dim. $\begin{smallmatrix}6\\4\end{smallmatrix}$ F Aug. 6   A♭ Major 6   D Major $\begin{smallmatrix}6\\4\end{smallmatrix}$

7. Draw each triad (in root position) according to the scale degree name.

Key of D Major

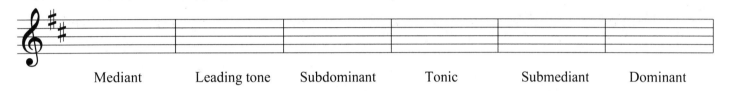

Mediant   Leading tone   Subdominant   Tonic   Submediant   Dominant

8. Identify the quality of each seventh chord (Major, Dominant, minor, half diminished or diminished).

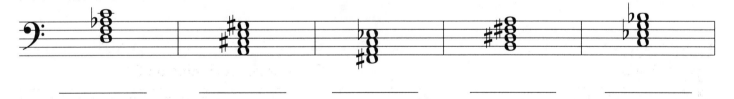

_____   _____   _____   _____   _____

9. Draw the dominant seventh chord for each key.

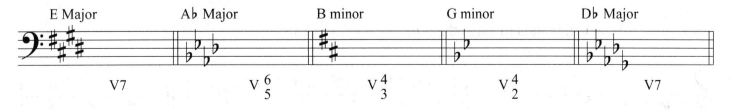

E Major   A♭ Major   B minor   G minor   D♭ Major

V7   V $\begin{smallmatrix}6\\5\end{smallmatrix}$ V $\begin{smallmatrix}4\\3\end{smallmatrix}$ V $\begin{smallmatrix}4\\2\end{smallmatrix}$ V7

GP669

10. Label each underlined chord with a Roman numeral and figured bass. Then, write the name
of each cadence on the lines above the staffs.

11. The music below modulates with a secondary dominant. Label each underlined chord with a
Roman numeral and figured bass and name the new key.

D Major: _____   _____   _____   _____   _____ of _____

_____ Major: _____   _____   _____   _____

12. This music excerpt is from a fugue by Bach. Study the music to answer the questions below.

From *Fugue in E Major, WTC Bk. 1, No. 9* by Bach

    a. How many voices are in this fugue? _____

    b. What is the texture of a fugue? _____

    c. Name the compositional device used with the entrance of each voice. _____